STATISTICS FOR MATHEMATICIANS

AN INTRODUCTION

STATISTICS
FOR
MATHEMATICIANS
AN INTRODUCTION

D. J. FINNEY

Professor of Statistics in the University of Edinburgh;
Director of the Agricultural Research Council's Unit of Statistics

OLIVER & BOYD

EDINBURGH AND LONDON

OLIVER AND BOYD LTD
Tweeddale Court
Edinburgh 1

39a Welbeck Street
London W1

First published 1968

Printed in Great Britain by
Spottiswoode, Ballantyne & Co. Ltd., London and Colchester

PREFACE

Every serious student of mathematics should be introduced to mathematical statistics, for this has been a major field of twentieth-century mathematical activity. Yet a suitable course must conform to several constraints. It must be short, in order to fit into a crowded curriculum. It must be an adequate component of education for the many whose studies will not go further in this direction, yet it must give the few a basis on which to opt for later specialisation in statistics. It must have sufficient mathematical content to be worthy of its place in the curriculum, and must avoid entirely pedestrian exercises in the reduction and presentation of numerical observations. It must maintain contact with the scientific applications that have stimulated growth of the subject, and therefore must avoid an excessively abstract and axiomatic approach. It should illustrate the manner in which many other branches of mathematics are woven into the fabric of statistics, yet it must not demand for its understanding a mathematical sophistication that is beyond the student at the time. It must encourage an interest in a field that at first can seem far removed from other mathematical teaching, yet—perhaps a deplorable but surely a realistic admission—it should provide scope for the testing of understanding by examination!

Despite the number of constraints, I believe that many different attempts to satisfy them could be made. Teachers of mathematics and statistics would benefit if they could choose between several approaches, yet I do not know any book that seeks to serve this end. I therefore put forward a very personal effort to achieve a proper balance. This book is intended as the text for a course of 10–20 lectures, to students with no previous knowledge of probability or statistics whose time for reading outside the classroom is severely restricted. In order to make the ideas accessible to a student early in his career, perhaps at the end of his first or at the start of his second undergraduate year, dependence on mathematical expertise has been kept to a minimum. This has been achieved by emphasising expression in mathematical terms and the underlying principles of the theory, but stating results of mathematical operations without full proof. An appendix provides details for the reader who wants them, but often these are unimportant to the main stream of the argument: those who go further in the study of statistics will acquire

v

the technical skill later. At the stage for which this course is intended, no student should be held back from understanding the use of sampling distributions by his inability to evaluate certain multiple integrals. Some more difficult or less essential sections, marked with an asterisk, may be omitted at first reading.

The book is written around a particular problem of experimental science, and frequent reference is made to the interplay of the biological problem and the statistical theory, but this should not be regarded as a rigid limitation on its use. The imaginative teacher might construct his lectures around a very different experiment, or even take some non-experimental problem of applied statistics as his recurrent theme, thus aiding students to appreciate a wider generality for the methodology based upon the book. The good student will learn far more if he sets himself to apply the ideas to other problems than if he never looks beyond the application of statistical theory to the effect of diet on the blood of rats.

If the twelve chapters introduce many students to probability, properties of frequency distributions of observations and of derived statistics, experimental design, estimation and statistical inference, and if as a consequence an occasional student resolves to specialise in statistics, they will have accomplished their purpose.

I am very grateful to my colleague, Miss Eryl Shirley, whose careful reading of the text has enabled me to correct a number of small errors.

Edinburgh
September 1967

D. J. FINNEY

CONTENTS

vii

* Sections so marked may be omitted at a first reading.

Chapter 1

INTRODUCTORY IDEAS

1.1 INTUITION AND DEFINITION

The word 'probable' is in the vocabulary of most users of English. Many have an intuitive appreciation of more exact concepts contained in the word *probability*, at least in respect of the ordering of uncertain events. The statement:

A snowfall is more probable on Christmas Day than on Midsummer Day

will be readily understood. Almost equivalent is the statement:

The probability that snow falls on Christmas Day is greater than the probability that it falls on Midsummer Day,

though this carries the undertone that perhaps the ordering of probabilities can be based upon numerical measures of probabilities for different events. Some will find no difficulty in the further step that permits such statements as:

The probability that this coin falls head upwards is $\frac{1}{2}$

and

The probability that snow falls in this town on Christmas Day is $\frac{2}{7}$.

In a society that gives much time and effort to gambling, the simpler laws of combining probabilities and drawing inferences with their aid should surely be widely comprehensible, though perhaps if understanding were widespread the profits of those who provide facilities for organised gambling would be less! The need for this understanding is deeper. Many of the policies and decisions of government today rest upon implicit or explicit comparisons of the probabilities of possible alternative consequences. Will an increased tax on a luxury increase or decrease total revenue? What effect will a new motorway have on the use of public

1

transport, the siting of industry, and on road accidents, and what is the optimal route? Where should new hospitals be built and what special facilities should they include, in order to serve best the needs of the community for the next 25–50 years? This dependence recurs in other organisations within our society, most obviously of course in insurance but also in the plans of an industry to satisfy the consumers of its products and in the management of a hotel for providing its various services effectively and economically. Even at the level of the family and the individual, each day brings decisions based upon uncertainties in which some intuitive assessment of probabilities may guide many whose mathematical knowledge is small: the planning of a child's education, the choice of a brand of paint for protecting the fabric of a house, and the daily choice of clothing for an uncertain climate all require at least a crude probabilistic argument.

These examples are complex and difficult, and this book is not designed to help directly with them. They are mentioned in order to emphasise that the problems of probability and statistics are not trivial in logic or in importance. The informed citizen of a democracy should accept a responsibility for being able to read critically arguments based upon probabilistic reasoning. The mathematician may well develop his understanding on a relatively formal system.

Even the definition of probability presents logical difficulties. A statement such as:

> If an event can happen in N equally likely ways, and R of these have a particular property, then the probability that the event that occurs has the property is R/N

is helpful. Here the meaning of *event* should be obvious: it is simply a convenient term for a happening that can recur and that can be classified in two or more different ways (e.g., a coin classified as heads or tails, or Christmas Day classified in respect of its weather at a specified place). This definition indicates, for example, that the probability of a fairly spun coin falling heads is $\frac{1}{2}$ ($N=2$, $R=1$) and the probability that a fairly thrown cubical die shows a face the number on which is a divisor of 18 is $\frac{2}{3}$ ($N=6$, $R=4$). However, phrases such as 'equally likely' and 'fairly thrown' are themselves meaningful only in terms of probability, and the supposed definition is circular. An alternative attempt is a statement such as:

> If an event observed n times manifests a particular property r of these times, then the probability that a particular instance of the event will have the property is the limit of r/n as n tends to infinity.

This again agrees with intuition for simple trials with coins and dice. and makes more sense in any discussion of the probability of a particular state of the weather on Christmas Day. However, it leaves open the question of whether or not r/n will approach any limit!

In a standard glossary of statistical terminology, Kendall and Buckland (1957) say of probability:

> A basic concept which may be taken either as undefinable, expressing in some way a 'degree of belief', or as the limiting frequency in an infinite random series . Both approaches have their difficulties and the most convenient axiomatisation of probability theory is a matter of personal taste. Fortunately both lead to much the same calculus of probabilities.

Those who are interested in the philosophy of mathematical thought may wish to pursue this further in publications concerned with the fundamental concepts of probability theory. Difficulties of formulating noncircular definitions of 'point' and 'line' have not prevented the development of the theory of geometry, nor have they inhibited its use in applied sciences. For the present purpose, probability will be similarly regarded as a measure of relative frequencies whose nature is intuitively appreciated and for which the simple rules of operation are obvious.

Probability is measured on a scale ranging from 0 to 1. The value 0 is the probability that an event with a particular property never occurs: for example, the probability that one throw of a standard die gives the result 13. Similarly 1 is the probability that the property is always present: for example, the probability that the die gives a number which is a divisor of 180. The value 0·137 corresponds to a property that one expects to find on average in 137 out of 1000 events in any very long series: of course it does not exclude the possibility that in a particular series of 2000 the property is found 273 times, 295 times, or even 695 times instead of 274 (see sections 4.1–4.6 and 5.2).

1.2 STATISTICS

When probability has been accepted as a concept, the laws of its combination can be developed and a large corpus of deductive theory can be studied. At the price of some additional logical difficulties, inductive theory is also obtainable. The one branch is concerned with deductions about relative frequencies of observations when probabilities are known; the other is concerned with inference about probabilities from records of observations. All this theory is intrinsically mathematical, it may be enthusiastically followed by some mathematicians and largely neglected by others as a matter of personal inclination: if its sole application were to games of chance with coins, dice, and like equipment, there it would rest.

This is not so; the analysis and interpretation of statistical records, and the planning for effective collection of statistical records, involve consideration of relative frequencies to which the laws of probability apply. Kendall and Buckland (1957) say of *statistics*:

> Numerical data relating to an aggregate of individuals; the science of collecting, analysing and interpreting such data.

The analysis and interpretation require something more than mathematics. Statistical records may consist of ages at death of members of a human population, or of weight increases of rats after eight weeks on different diets, or of yields of oranges from individual trees of three different varieties, or of numbers of shirts rejected as unsuitable for sale on each day of work in a clothing factory for one year. In any one of these series, the individual values will differ among themselves. If the nature of this variation can be described in terms of probabilities, then the analysis can employ probability theory. Conceivably, with suitable units of measurements for the first three, the four sets of records might be numerically identical: 73, 14, 37, 1, 37, 60, ...; even at a superficial level, however, the four processes giving rise to these numbers and the logical interrelations of the observations are so dissimilar that entirely different descriptions and formulations of the probability structure are needed. Choice of the appropriate formulation, often termed the *mathematical model*, requires experience of the type of problem, judgement, assessment of the consequences of using a model that is only an approximation to reality, and other non-mathematical considerations. All these are integral to the activities of the statistician. Moreover, the fact that the origin of the numerical records affects materially their analysis and interpretation is a good reason for consulting a statistician at the stage of planning an investigation rather than only at the end.

Statistical science has developed rapidly during the past 50 years. Much of the stimulus to growth has come from diverse fields of science and technology, from agriculture and genetics, from pharmacology and animal ecology, from clinical medicine and the manufacturing industries. Yet growth would have been impossible without a wide range of mathematical skills: combinatorial theory and integral calculus, multidimensional geometry and theory of the complex variable, simple arithmetic and the programming of electronic computers, matrices and groups. Although statistics should not be considered a branch of mathematics, the close connection with probability theory and the variety of mathematical techniques employed give the subject an intrinsic interest and importance for mathematicians. The importance of recent theoretical developments in this field justifies a belief that a short course in probability and statistics should be an integral part of any degree in mathematics. This is important both as contributing to a balanced view of modern mathematics and as introducing students to a field in which some may later choose to specialise.

1.3. THE RAW MATERIAL OF STATISTICS

The science of statistics is concerned with the reporting and interpretation of numerical information. This information can come from any kind of counting or measuring, the essential feature being that a set of records refers to a number of comparable members of a *population* or a *universe*. The individual numerical value from a population is often termed an *observation*. The weight of a man or the number of cars completed by a factory last year is not a piece of statistical information unless it is under discussion as a member of a population; relevant populations might be the weights of all men in a city, the weights of one man at weekly intervals over several years, the numbers of cars completed last year at other factories, and the numbers of cars from the same factory in each of the past 20 years. The notion of a population from which statistical information has been obtained is essential. Moreover, as the examples given have indicated, one observation may be regarded as belonging to each of several populations. The manner in which the observation is presented and interpreted will depend on the reference population, and on how the particular observation was selected from the population (Chapter 7).

A population may be *finite* or *infinite*. All possible numbers of deaths in an experiment on 30 mice or the ages of all students graduating from a particular university in 1968 constitute a finite population. So do the weights of all adult males in a city, although, even if attention is restricted to one moment of time, there may be difficulties of definition and determination of who is within the city. On the other hand, all possible lengths of line of one metre or less, the areas of all regular polygons that can be inscribed in a circle of unit radius, or the possible percentages of fat in individual pint bottles of milk are infinite populations. Many populations that strictly are finite can be regarded as infinite for most practical purposes, so permitting the use of theory applicable to limits. For example, the weights of all adult males in Belgium on 1 May 1967, or the numbers of cigarettes smoked by these men on the same day, are sufficiently large populations to be considered infinite. (Although the number of cigarettes must be an integer in the range 0 to some upper bound such as 150, most of these will be repeated many times for different men.) Even a purely conceptual population may in some respects seem finite but be most usefully treated as infinite, an example being the percentage sugar in the blood of *all* rats of a specified laboratory strain at 12 weeks of age, 'all' being taken to include past, present and future.

The quantity under consideration may be a *continuous variate* or a *discrete variate*, terms which are almost self-explanatory. A continuous variate is one measured on a continuous scale—weights, lengths, times, densities, percentage nitrogen in plant material. The commonest discrete or discontinuous variate is that consisting of the positive integers, which arise in all observations recorded as counts—the numbers of residents in individual houses, the numbers of faulty articles produced by a factory day by day. Negative integers may be included, as in a variate which is the increase in the number of pupils in each of the schools of a city between 1956 and 1966. However, a discrete variate does not need to be restricted to integers; the percentage of deaths in an experiment on 27 mice and the price of an armchair expressed in £ and fractions of a £ are both discrete variates (the first can take only the 28 values 0, 3·70, 7·41, 11·11, ..., 96·30, 100).

Some purists insist that all actual measurements are discrete, in that every instrument used has a limit of discrimination: one may be able to distinguish between lengths of 15·73 mm and 15·74 mm but not to record any intermediate magnitudes. In practice this is unimportant unless very coarsely graduated instruments are in use. Occasionally a conversion of a continuous variate to a discrete is convenient, for example by expressing ages to the nearest year or in five-year intervals. On the other hand, in some statistical procedures, a discrete variate can conveniently be treated as continuous; this is particularly so for large integers, for example the numbers of aphids on individual plants or the numbers of red cells in sample millilitres of blood.

1.4 DATA

Statisticians frequently refer to numerical records which they are asked to analyse as *data*. They should remember that the word means 'given'; experimenters who have spent hours or months on a piece of research, or economists who have collected information on household incomes and expenditures by laborious inquiry, may sometimes resent the implication that what is given is obtained without cost! Insistence that the word 'data' be not used would be pedantry, but all concerned with statistics should regard its etymology as a warning that hard-won data deserve respect. One task of the statistician is to ensure that any analysis he supplies is efficient in relation to the cost of time and labour of securing the data; he must eschew both an analysis that fails to extract the full information contained in the data and one that is over-sophisticated for the needs of rather crude data.

Those who write about 'data' should remember that this noun is plural!

1.5 PLAN OF BOOK

Many excellent textbooks of mathematical statistics exist, and the only excuse for a book such as this is the intention of doing something different. No attempt is made here to cater for the student or other reader who is already determined to acquire a substantial knowledge of statistical theory, whether as a preliminary to becoming a professional statistician or as an adjunct to other qualifications. The demand for statisticians of all kinds is high, however, and many young mathematicians are attracted into other fields of specialisation before learning anything about statistics.

This book is written in the belief that university courses for pure mathematicians should include some introduction to mathematical statistics, ideally about half-way through the undergraduate teaching, at a time when the student has a reasonable mastery of technique but has not begun intensive specialisation. The time available will usually be small, perhaps 8–15 hours of lectures. Within this time, the student should be given a representative sample of statistical ideas, with emphasis on the variety of branches of pure mathematics involved and on the welding of these into a new discipline. For the most part rigour is unnecessary, and even much of the detail of mathematical manipulation can be set aside so as not to detract from the clear presentation of what is novel in thought and application.

In an attempt to give coherence to what could easily become a disjointed series of lectures or a number of disconnected essays, the theory is here presented with particular reference to an experimental situation. The experiment described in Chapter 2 and its two simplifications require for adequate discussion so many aspects of statistical science that their use as a central theme serves well to illustrate the essential unity of the subject. Moreover, the experimental situation should be comprehensible to any student with some scientific training. Many digressions will be introduced in order to avoid a presentation too highly specific to one problem of applied statistics, but every major idea introduced is in this book because it has some relevance to Chapter 2.

No claim is made that the topics included are all of primary importance. Indeed a similar book might be built around some very different problem of applied statistics, for example a survey of $0 \cdot 1$ per cent of the population for the investigation of recent health experience or records of telephone traffic at a busy switchboard over a period of several years. The topics included would then be a different cross-section of statistical science, having only a few in common with this book, but the whole discussion could be equally satisfactory in introducing the subject to the student.

Statistical theory makes frequent demands on mathematical techniques such as summation of series, differentiation of complicated functions, evaluation of simple and multiple integrals, solution of equations, and manipulations of combinatorial algebra. The reader is assumed to have some familiarity with these, though his skill may be limited. To show full details in the text every time that a bit of mathematical technology is required would distract attention from the statistical argument. Usually, therefore, once a problem has been stated in mathematical symbolism only the result is shown in the text; the reader to whom the intermediate steps are not obvious, and who is properly inquisitive, will find the details in Appendix A. In the text, a reference such as (A11–A14) indicates that the steps omitted can be found as equations (11) to (14) of this Appendix (sometimes with a change of notation), but that the main text can be read uninterruptedly by those prepared to take the details on trust.

For this very elementary introduction, some of the more advanced branches of mathematics important to statistical theory and practice (matrix algebra, finite geometries, complex variable, measure theory, etc.) have been avoided almost entirely. One or two results dependent upon them have been stated with little explanation.

1.6   NOTATION

Although efforts have been made to maintain consistency of terminology and unambiguous use of symbols throughout the book, perfection is not practicable. The subject is so diverse in its needs that the condition that no symbol is ever used in two different senses could be bought only at the price of great complexity of alphabets and suffixes. The scientist or technologist who requires to apply statistical methods to his own problems often finds confusion arising from the notation and symbols, his troubles being aggravated by the different practices adopted by different authors of standard texts.

To the mathematician, however, a symbol familiar in one context that occurs elsewhere with entirely different meaning should cause no trouble provided that its meaning is clearly stated each time. To consider use of E as a functional symbol for expectation in Section 4.5 a ban against employing it as fifth member of the sequence A, B, C, D, E in Chapter 11 would be a ridiculous constraint. If, d, e were invariably to refer to differentiation and to $2 \cdot 718\,28 \dots$ respectively, the restriction on sensible choice of symbols would be severe. An attempt has been made to keep some symbols reasonably fixed in meaning (ξ, σ, s, $\bar{x}$, P, M, etc.), but to leave others free for current use in any convenient manner (u, v, a, K, etc.). This is not an absolute rule. In general, a symbol is always to be understood as having the meaning that has most recently been explicitly stated, unless the context makes a different meaning obvious (as may happen with d or e).

Chapter 2

EXPERIMENTS

2.1 The Main Experiment

University Departments of Statistics are involved both in teaching the subject and in advancing research into its theory. If they are to avoid the error of regarding statistics solely as a branch of abstract mathematics, they need to do much more. In particular, they should be concerned with providing statistical help for other sciences. Not only is advice likely to be sought on how to analyse data from experiments, but often a scientist asks for suggestions on the planning of an experiment in order that results may be as precise as possible.

The following is a modified version of one inquiry that came to the Department of Statistics in the University of Aberdeen:

A physiologist proposes to compare three alternative treatments, A, B, C, in respect of their effects on the rate at which red blood cells of rats take up oxygen. Treatments A, B are alternative supplements to a standard diet; C is a surgical procedure. As a basis for comparison, some rats are to be maintained on the standard diet without surgery, and this will be termed 'treatment' D. Each rat is to receive its treatment as soon as it is weaned, and to continue for a fixed period of weeks on the appropriate diet. In order to determine oxygen uptake, a rat must be killed and its blood used immediately. The uptake must be measured by passing oxygen through a fixed volume of blood for 4 hours; the physiologist can prepare and use only one animal at a time, and so can measure only two rats per day.

The physiologist is primarily interested in differences between mean oxygen uptakes for A, B, C, D, but he wishes also to examine sex differences and to see whether treatments affect both sexes equally. Information on differences between litters and on time trends may be useful in the planning of future experiments.

10

The animals available for the experiment are 32 in all, 4 litters of 8 animals with 4 males and 4 females in each litter. How should the experiment be designed, and how should the results be analysed?

2.2 TERMINOLOGY

In discussion of statistical aspects of experimentation, the word *treatment* is the general term used for a characteristic chosen by the experimenter and imposed on the experimental subjects or units (here each unit is a rat). The word refers always to something that is to be compared with one or more alternative treatments, and a characteristic imposed on all the individuals in an experiment (such as a standard diet or uniform pattern of cage) is not a treatment. A treatment, in fact, is under trial as a primary object of experimental study, and may be any specified combination of factors describing the diet, surgery, management, etc., of an animal. Moreover, for convenience of nomenclature, what is frequently described as a *control*, the absence of any dietary supplement or the absence of surgery (*D* in section 2.1), may also be termed a treatment. If an experiment is intended to compare natural characteristics of the experimental subjects (such as sex, age, colour of coat) the word treatment may be used also for these.

The final sentence of section 2.1 refers to the *design* of the experiment. The design is the system of rules that determines how the available animals are to be allocated to treatments, which animals are to be killed for measurement of oxygen uptake on each day of the experiment, and other matters concerned with the ordering and conduct of the experiment. Frequent comments on points of design will be made, for this is an important aspect of statistical science and Chapter 11 is especially concerned with it.

2.3 CONSTRAINTS OF DESIGN

The reader unfamiliar with biological experimentation may wonder why special mention has been made of the number of rats whose oxygen uptake can be measured in one day, the classification of the rats by litter and sex, and so on. The reason is that these factors may affect the magnitude of the measured quantity. Animals of like sex or of common parentage are frequently found to be more similar in measurable properties than animals differing in these factors. Results from a complex measuring procedure used for a prolonged period may show progressive changes, quite independent of any true differences in the substances measured, because of change in the standards of the operator or unsuspected changes in the procedure or instruments used in it. These things do not necessarily happen; they happen sufficiently often for it to be desirable so to plan experiments that comparisons between treatments are balanced in respect of them. If the rats allotted to treatment A were predominantly males from two litters and those allotted to C were predominantly females from the other two litters, any apparent difference between the surgical and the first dietary treatment suggested by measurements of oxygen uptake might be in reality a reflection of a sex difference or of an inherent difference between litters. Satisfactory balancing is sometimes very easily achieved, sometimes much less easily. Chapter 11 contains an account of some of the possibilities, but many other references will occur.

2.4   A Simplified Experiment

The experiment of section 2.1 presents too many difficulties for the early chapters of this book. Two simpler problems will be used instead. The first is:

> A physiologist proposes to compare two alternative treatments, A, D, in respect of their effects on the rate at which red blood cells of rats take up oxygen. Treatment A is a standard diet with a special supplement, and D is the standard diet alone. Each rat is to receive one or other of these treatments for a fixed period of weeks, beginning at weaning. In order to measure oxygen uptake, a rat must be killed and its blood used immediately. The uptake is measured by passing oxygen through a fixed volume of blood for 4 hours. Thus the determination for one rat occupies the physiologist for about $4\frac{1}{2}$ hours: the physiologist can therefore measure only two rats per day.
>
> The animals available for the experiment are 32 male rats, two from each of 16 litters. How should the experiment be designed, and how should the results be analysed?

2.5   An Alternative Simplified Experiment

The second version of the simplified experiment is exactly like the first in its specification of treatments and method of measuring oxygen uptake by the blood. The first paragraph of the description in section 2.4 stands, and is followed by:

> The animals available for the experiment are 32 male rats, equal in age but with no information enabling them to be classified by litter.

How should the experiment be designed, and how should the results be analysed?

2.6   USE OF THE EXPERIMENTS

As mentioned in section 1.5, the presentation of statistical theory and method that follows is largely built around the three experiments described above. These will be distinguished as Experiments ONE (section 2.1), TWO (section 2.4) and THREE (section 2.5).

Chapter 3

PROBABILITY, IN PRACTICE AND THEORY

3.1 Null Hypotheses and Significance Tests

The three experiments used as a central theme for this book have been described in Chapter 2. For the purpose of introducing some elementary ideas on probability, Experiment TWO is the most suitable. In the light of what has been said in section 2.3, the simple step of allotting one rat from each pair to treatment A and the other to D may be seen to secure a desirable balance. Suppose this done, and suppose the oxygen uptake for every rat to have been measured. For the present, no attempt will be made to analyse numerical values. Instead, the data will be reduced to the simpler form of records of which rat in each pair had the higher rate: as a convention, the result for a pair will be recorded as α or δ according as treatment A or treatment D showed the higher rate. Although an experimental scientist would rarely be content to have his careful measurements neglected in this manner, for some types of data nothing more than this may be available: if treated animals are classified in terms of healthiness, agility or beauty, a record of which of a pair has the quality in greater degree may be all that can be made.

An important form of argument is the test of statistical significance (section 5.2), closely analogous to the *reductio ad absurdum* of elementary geometry. If the two treatments do not differ in their influences on rate of oxygen uptake, for any pair of animals the record is as likely to be α as δ (the chance of exact equality is negligibly small if the measurements have been made with high accuracy). Since a probability of 1 represents certainty (section 1.1), and one of α, δ is certain to occur, the probability of α is $\frac{1}{2}$, or

$$Pr(\alpha) = Pr(\delta) = \tfrac{1}{2}. \tag{3.1}$$

The 16 pairs are independent of one another. A predominance of α in the records, such as 15 out of 16, would cast doubt on equation (3.1) and

14

would therefore encourage a belief that, relative to D, A increases the rate of oxygen uptake.

A more formal approach is to state what is called a *null hypothesis*. Here, for example, one states 'Treatments A and D do not differ in their effects on oxygen uptake.' If this be true, symmetry shows equation (3.1) to be one obvious consequence. Can this be used in a study of the relative frequencies with which the 17 possible outcomes (16α and 0δ; 15 and 1; 14, 2; ...; 0, 16) from the 16 pairs are to be expected? As will be seen in section 4.2, it can. Suppose a particular experiment to have yielded the outcome 11α, 5δ. If calculation were to show that outcomes at least as extreme as this (in respect of departure from the equality of α and δ suggested by the null hypothesis) would occur only exceedingly rarely, grave suspicion would fall on the null hypothesis. On the other hand, if calculations were to show that the relative frequency of so extreme a result is quite large, no great suspicion would arise. Such relative frequencies can be calculated (sections 3.7, 5.1, 5.2). It is usual to specify in advance a fairly small probability, such as 0·05, and to make comparison with this. The comparison is termed a *test of statistical significance*: if the probability of a result at least as extreme is smaller than the chosen value, there is said to be statistically significant evidence against the null hypothesis, which is thereupon rejected, whereas if the probability exceeds that value the evidence is non-significant.

These ideas will become clearer with the aid of a more detailed discussion of Experiment TWO, but consideration of how to combine probabilities is first necessary.

3.2   SAMPLE SPACE

The notion of a *sample space*, used to represent the possible outcomes of an experiment or observation, can help the appreciation of rules to be presented in sections 3.4, 3.5. As a trivial example, suppose that an experiment consists of throwing a coin and a cubical die simultaneously. The 12 possible combinations of face of coin and the numbers 1 to 6 can be represented by a two-dimensional sample space containing a point for each of the 12 mutually exclusive *events* (Fig. 3.1). With each point can be associated its probability. In Fig. 3.1, if coin and die were well-balanced and fairly thrown each point would have probability 1/12; if the die were biased in favour of 2, the second column of points would have probabilities greater than 1/12 and the others less than 1/12; if the coin were double-headed, the upper row of points would have probabilities 1/6 and the lower 0!

More than two dimensions may easily be required. For example, students chosen at random from the undergraduates of a university could be recorded according to sex, faculty, and year, and these facts could be represented in a three-dimensional space. For discrete variates, only specified distinct points need be recognised, but for continuous variates a continuum of points is needed in the obvious manner. The age (x_1), height (x_2) and weight (x_3) of a student require representation by a point (x_1, x_2, x_3) in a three-dimensional continuum. A meteorological record for a day, consisting perhaps of maximum and minimum air temperature, hours of sunshine, rainfall and barometric pressure at noon, could be regarded as specifying a point in a five-dimensional sample space. All the six characteristics of a student mentioned above could be represented in a six-dimensional space that is part continuous, part discrete. Although no physical models of these last two spaces are possible, general geometric terms are still convenient for their description.

If the distinction between the 16 pairs is to be preserved, Experiment TWO requires a 16-dimensional space, 2^{16} points in the form of a hypercube with each dimension having the two possibilities α, δ. Alternatively, one dimension of 17 points can represent simply the total number of α's in the experiment, 0, 1, ..., 16; this loses some of the detail of the results, but may retain all the information that matters (section 4.2).

Continuous variates and a continuous sample space can be regarded throughout as limits of the corresponding discrete variates and space. As already explained, if all variates are discrete, each point of the sample space has a probability associated with it and the total over all points is unity. For continuous variates, integration replaces summation in the usual manner. If all variates are continuous, the probability associated with each point of the sample space is an infinitesimal element, such that the multiple integral in respect of all the variates over the space is unity. For a single variate, the nature of this simple integration should be evident. In the example of ages, heights and weights of students, a probability element for x_1, x_2, x_3 would integrate over all (or all positive) x_1, x_2, x_3 to give unity. Indeed, very little knowledge of the characteristics of students indicates that narrower limits could be used without altering the situation: the integral taken over $15 < x_1 < 65$ (in years), $100 < x_2 < 230$ (in cm), $30 < x_3 < 200$ (in kg) would suffice, as the probability outside those ranges would be zero. If the sample space is a mixture of continuous and discrete variates, a corresponding mixture of summation and integration will apply; this may be awkward to describe, but is sufficiently obvious in character to need no further comment here.

3.3 COMBINATION OF PROBABILITIES

A common need is to express the probability of some class of events, or of a composite event, in terms of known or specified probabilities for single events. In the coin and die experiment of section 3.2, one might wish to determine the probability that the coin shows 'head' and the die an odd number, symbolized perhaps by Pr(H, odd), in terms of the 12 probabilities for different possible results of the experiment. Again,

Fig. 3.1. Sample space for coin and die.

one might wish to know the probability that a student selected from the population mentioned in section 3.2 is over 40 years old, or over 40 years and between 60 kg and 80 kg in weight, irrespective of height.

If probability is interpreted in terms of relative frequency (section 1.1), reference to the sample space enables the correct procedures to be readily understood. In fact, for discrete variates all that is required is summation of the probabilities associated with appropriate points of the sample space. For example, Fig. 3.1 contains only three points that satisfy the requirement 'H, odd', and since these are mutually exclusive results the required relative frequency is the sum of the relative frequencies for the three points; in an obvious symbolism

$$Pr(\text{H, odd}) = Pr(\text{H, 1}) + Pr(\text{H, 3}) + Pr(\text{H, 5}). \qquad (3.2)$$

Similarly, the probability that the die shows 5 or more irrespective of the face of the coin may be written

$$Pr(-, \geqslant 5) = Pr(\text{H, 5}) + Pr(\text{H, 6}) + Pr(\text{T, 5}) + Pr(\text{T, 6}), \qquad (3.3)$$

by summation over the four points of the sample space that meet the requirement. If coin and die were well-balanced and fairly thrown, the probabilities become 3/12 (or 1/4) and 4/12 (or 1/3) respectively, but they need not take these values under other conditions.

For continuous variates, summation of probabilities must be replaced by integration over appropriate parts of the sample space, $\int_{40}^{65} \int_{100}^{230} \int_{30}^{200}$ or

$\int\limits_{40}^{65} \int\limits_{100}^{230} \int\limits_{60}^{80}$ for the student population. This will be made more explicit in section 4.8; at present, the argument is developed in relation to discrete variates, although many results remain true for continuous variates.

The mutual exclusiveness of the events is essential to the above argument, and the more general situation must now be considered. Suppose that A and B are two classes of events, each defined as the occurrence of one of a subset of possibilities in the sample space. Then the whole sample space can be represented diagrammatically as a closed contour, within which two smaller (and possibly overlapping) regions

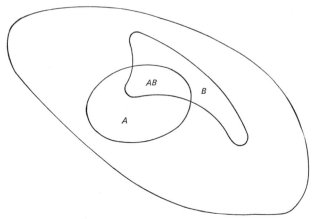

Fig. 3.2. Illustration of two classes of events within a sample space; AB denotes the part of the space common to class A and class B.

represent A and B (Fig. 3.2). For example, if the sample space is that for two dice thrown simultaneously, the classes might be:

    A is 'value shown by die 2 is divisible by that for die 1',

    B is 'total of two dice is greater than or equal to 7'.

The space then contains 36 discrete points, and those belonging to A or B can be found by examining each point (Fig. 3.3).

The following notation is convenient:

    $A+B$ denotes occurrence of at least one of A and B, i.e. 'A or B or both';

    AB denotes occurrence of both A and B;

Pr(A)   denotes the probability that any event known to be in the sample space in fact lies within the subset *A*;

Pr(A|B) denotes the *conditional probability* that an event *known* to be within the subset *B* is within the subset *A*; that is to say, it is the relative frequency of *A* among events known to be *B*, and for its calculation *B* plays the role of the sample space.

Two theorems then follow. If the meaning of Figs. 3.2, 3.3 is understood, the truth of each is self-evident, whatever the probabilities associated with points of the sample space.

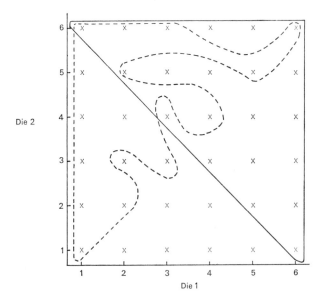

Fig. 3.3. Sample space for 36 events possible when 2 dice are thrown

‒ ‒ ‒ boundary of region for events of class *A* ⎫ as defined
——— boundary of region for events of class *B* ⎭ in §3.3.

3.4   ADDITION THEOREM

For any two subsets, *A* and *B*, of the sample space,

$$Pr(A+B) = Pr(A)+Pr(B)-Pr(AB). \qquad (3.4)$$

Reference to Fig. 3.2 makes proof immediate.

In the example, if the dice are well-balanced, counts of points show that

$$Pr(A) = \tfrac{14}{36},$$
$$Pr(B) = \tfrac{21}{36},$$
$$Pr(A+B) = \tfrac{29}{36},$$
$$Pr(AB) = \tfrac{6}{36},$$

and

$$29 = 14+21-6.$$

The truth of (3.4), however, does not depend upon the points having equal probabilities; whatever the probabilities attached to individual points of the sample space, the proof stands.

An important special case arises if no points of the sample space are common to A and B, which might be written

$$AB = 0.$$

In the space of Fig. 3.3, one might have A being 'total of two dice does not exceed 4' and B being 'total of two dice is 8', in place of the A, B specified in section 3.3; a rather more complicated example, for which the reader should draw his own diagram, has A 'total of two dice is odd and greater or equal to 7' and B 'die 1 exceeds die 2 and the difference is divisible by 4'. If A, B are in this sense *mutually exclusive*,

$$Pr(AB) = 0.$$

Then, and **only** then,

$$Pr(A+B) = P(A)+P(B). \tag{3.5}$$

3.5 MULTIPLICATION THEOREM

For any two subsets of the sample space,

$$Pr(AB) = Pr(A)\,Pr(B|A) = Pr(B)\,Pr(A|B). \tag{3.6}$$

This is seen immediately because the definition of $P(A|B)$ is equivalent to

$$Pr(A|B) = \frac{Pr(AB)}{Pr(B)}. \tag{3.7}$$

For the example, with well-balanced dice,

$$Pr(AB) = \tfrac{14}{36}\times\tfrac{6}{14} = \tfrac{1}{6},$$
$$Pr(AB) = \tfrac{21}{36}\times\tfrac{6}{21} = \tfrac{1}{6}.$$

If the probability of A is unaltered by knowledge of whether or not B occurs, so that

$$Pr(A) = Pr(A|B),$$

the classes of event are said to be *independent*. Then and **only** then

$$Pr(AB) = Pr(A)Pr(B). \qquad (3.8)$$

For example, if the sample space for two dice is inspected in relation to

A: 'die 1 shows 2 or 5',

B: 'total of two dice is greater or equal to 7',

one sees that

$$Pr(B) = \tfrac{21}{36},$$
$$Pr(B|A) = \tfrac{7}{12},$$

and therefore A, B are independent.

3.6   COMMENTS ON THEOREMS

The addition and multiplication theorems remain true when the variates are continuous and quantities such as $Pr(B)$ involve integration over a region of the sample space.

Both theorems extend readily to three or more classes of events. If C is a third subset of the sample space,

$$Pr(A+B+C) = Pr(A)+Pr(B)+Pr(C)-Pr(AB)-Pr(AC)$$
$$-Pr(BC)+Pr(ABC), \qquad (3.9)$$

and

$$Pr(ABC) = Pr(A).Pr(B|A).Pr(C|AB). \qquad (3.10)$$

Proofs are simple, by repeated application of the theorems.

Two of the commonest sources of error in statistical inference are the use of (3.5) when A, B are not mutually exclusive and the use of (3.8) when A, B are not independent. When the nature of observational data makes $Pr(AB)$ or $Pr(A|B)$ difficult to determine, the temptation to make a simplifying assumption can be great, but grossly fallacious argument and conclusions may follow. The reader should guard himself against excessive enthusiasm for drawing conclusions from inadequate records, and against the wiles of cunning examiners! Positive evidence for exclusiveness or independence is always required before (3.5) or (3.8) is used.

3.7   PARAMETERS

In many situations, probabilities are not known numerically but are specified in terms of one or more parameters. For example, in Experiment TWO without asserting the null hypothesis (section 3.1) it might be

2

reasonable to assert that in respect of repetitions of the experiment on sets of 16 pairs of rats

$$Pr(\alpha) = 1 - Pr(\delta) = P, \qquad (3.11)$$

where the *parameter P* is a constant for all pairs. (One could be even more general by invoking 16 parameters, one for each pair, but this is scarcely useful.) The multiplication theorem then enables other probabilities to be expressed as functions of P.

This experiment would normally be so conducted as to ensure independence of the results for different pairs. For example, the investigator would avoid any systematic allocation of the heavier, the more active, or the longer-tailed animal of each pair to treatment D, or any systematic pattern of measurement such that oxygen uptake is measured for D rats in mornings and A rats in afternoons (see Chapter 7). As long as this is ensured by the rules of conduct adopted by the investigator, equation (3.8) applies. Then, for example,

$$Pr \text{ (First and second pair } \alpha) = P^2,$$
$$Pr \text{ (First pair } \alpha, \text{ second } \delta) = P(1-P),$$
$$Pr \text{ (First pair } \delta, \text{ second } \alpha) = P(1-P),$$

and by generalisation

$$Pr \text{ (Pairs 1, 4, 7, 8, 13 are } \delta, \text{ others } \alpha) = P^{11}(1-P)^5.$$

Again, suppose that a reputedly cubical die is in reality a rectangular parallelepiped with unequal sides. The six faces will no longer have equal probabilities of appearing uppermost, though under fair conditions symmetry indicates equal probabilities for opposite faces. The physical properties of the die may now be expected to determine the probabilities for the faces as complicated functions of three parameters, $\theta_1, \theta_2, \theta_3$, the three linear dimensions of the die.

3.8   ESTIMATION AND STATISTICS

The null hypothesis for Experiment TWO is equivalent to assertion of a particular value for the parameter in (3.11):

$$P = \tfrac{1}{2}, \qquad (3.12)$$

a statement equivalent to equation (3.1). The significance test involves examination of whether experimental results are such as might reasonably be obtained when this is the true value of P.

An alternative approach, in some respects equivalent but with important logical differences, is to use the data in order to estimate the unknown parameter. This involves formulating a rule whereby a calculation is to be performed on the data in order to give a numerical value which can be regarded as estimating P. Any formula for calculating a numerical value from data is termed a *statistic*, and when a statistic is to be used in order to suggest the value of a parameter it is termed an *estimator*.

Suppose that in Experiment TWO the total number of α records from the 16 pairs is a. Then the statistic

$$p = a/16 \qquad (3.13)$$

has an intuitive appeal as an estimator of P. This is almost too obvious to need discussion, but there are other situations where choice of an appropriate statistic is less obvious. Even here, suppose a_1, a_2 are the numbers of α records for the first 12 and the last 10 pairs respectively. Then the statistics

$$\frac{a_1}{12}, \quad \frac{a_2}{10}, \quad \frac{1}{2}\left(\frac{a_1}{12}+\frac{a_2}{10}\right), \quad \frac{a_1+a_2}{22}, \quad \left[\frac{a_1 a_2}{120}\right]^{\frac{1}{2}}$$

are all at least plausible estimators of P. In this instance, the superiority of p may seem intuitively obvious; no objective choice is possible, however, until after recognition and general specification of the desirable properties of an estimator. Indeed, some criteria of the quality of estimation are needed before such manifest absurdities as

$$\frac{a}{19}, \quad \frac{a^2+a_1+5}{a_2+10}, \quad \frac{a_1^2+a_2^2}{12^2+10^2}, \quad a_1-a_2, \quad e^{-a}$$

can be dismissed from consideration. These last of course have little in common except that all are statistics.

The desirable properties of an estimator must take some account of relevance (why should e^{-a} bear any relation to P ?), of bias (will $a/19$ tend to be smaller than P ?), and of closeness of approach to the parameter (will $a_2/10$ tend to deviate from P to a greater extent than $a/16$?). For any particular set of data, even an apparently absurd estimator might chance to be almost exactly equal to P (although in real life this could rarely be known), and the properties must be considered in relation to the statistical behaviour of each estimator over repetitions of the observational or experimental programme. To express these ideas exactly is more difficult than to discuss the framework of tests of significance, and further consideration is deferred until Chapter 12.

EXERCISES

3.1 Prove equations (3.9), (3.10), making clear how they follow from the addition and multiplication theorems. Write down at least two alternative forms of equation (3.10), using different conditional probabilities, and state how many forms there are in all.

3.2 The probability that any one birth is male is P, a quantity close to but not necessarily equalling 0·5, and the probabilities for births on different occasions are independent. A family contains four children, none of whom are twins. Find (as a function of P) the total probability that the family includes two boys and two girls under each of the following conditions:

    (i) no other information is available;
    (ii) it is known that the eldest child is a boy;
    (iii) it is known that the eldest child is a girl;
    (iv) it is known that at least one child is a boy;
    (v) it is known that the family contains at least one boy and at least one girl.

3.3 Five sheep in a field are named P, Q, R, S, T; of these, P, Q, R are white and S, T black. A selection of three sheep is made in such a way that every possible set of three names has the same probability. By enumerating all possible cases or otherwise, find the probability that the selected sheep are 2 white and 1 black. Find also the conditional probability of such a selection under each of the following conditions:

    (i) it is known that the selected sheep include at least one black;
    (ii) it is known that the selected sheep include at least one white;
    (iii) it is known that the selected sheep include at least two white;
    (iv) it is known that the sheep left in the field are not all of one colour.

3.4 Find formulae for some generalisations of 3.3 above, first of all having w white and b black sheep in the field instead of 3 and 2, then selecting s instead of 3, and then introducing more general conditions.

3.5 At one counter of a certain bank, six clerks are normally on duty; these are Miss A, Miss B, and four men, W, X, Y, Z. Customers go indiscriminately to any of the counter positions at which a clerk is present, so that all have the same chance of being occupied.

At a particular moment, four clerks are occupied with customers. List all possible sets of four, and state the probability for each one of these. Hence evaluate the probability that the clerks with customers are one woman and three men. By considering appropriate regions of the sample space, find the conditional probability of the four clerks being one woman and three men under each of the following conditions in turn:

(i) it is known that W and Z are occupied;

(ii) it is known that at least two men (names unknown) are occupied;

(iii) it is known that W, X and Z are occupied;

(iv) it is known that at least three men (names unknown) are occupied;

(v) it is known that W is occupied;

(vi) it is known that W is not occupied;

(vii) it is known that W and Z are not occupied;

(viii) it is known that Miss A and W are occupied;

(ix) it is known that Miss A and W are not occupied;

(x) Miss B is making tea;

(xi) Two clerks (names unknown) are on holiday;

(xii) Miss B is making tea and Y is occupied.

[Adapted from Aberdeen, 1966]

3.6 A certain examination in History classifies 65 per cent of students as passing and 35 per cent as failing. It is proposed to replace this examination by a short test that will give the same result for 80 per cent of the students in each category but will indicate failure for 20 per cent who ought to pass and pass for 20 per cent who ought to fail. What proportion of all students would pass the short test? What is the probability that a student who passes the short test would also have passed the full examination?

[Adapted from Harvard, 1966]

3.7 In an area of good housing, assessors appraise the rateable value of houses correctly for 1/3 of the houses, £700 too high for 1/3 of the houses, and £700 too low for 1/3. By accident, two assessors (A and B) appraised a number of houses independently. The value assigned to each house was chosen as the lower of the two figures wherever there was disagreement.

Construct diagrams to show the sample space, and the probability associated with each point of it, for

(i) the pair of valuations made by assessors A, B;

(ii) the final rateable value assigned;

(iii) the rateable value assigned if the average of A and B were adopted;

for those houses whose 'correct' values are exactly £7000.

[Adapted from Harvard, 1966]

3.8 A psychologist receives from a laboratory twelve experimental mice all very similar in appearance. He is notified that three are of strain V, nine of strain W, and he knows a simple test for recognising the strain. If he tests mice one at a time, what is the probability that in order to identify the three mice of strain V he must test exactly (i) three mice, (ii) four mice, (iii) nine mice?

[Adapted from Harvard, 1966]

3.9 Three tennis matches are arranged for players A, B, C. In the first two matches, A is to play B and C in succession; his probabilities of winning are $2/3$ and $3/4$ respectively. In the third match B is to play C, and B's probability of winning is $2/3$.

For each player separately, find the probability that he wins exactly one match. Find also the probability that the tournament ends with all three players having won one match and lost one. If you are told that one player (unnamed) won two matches, find the conditional probabilities for each of the six possible sets of results.

[Adapted from Edinburgh, 1966]

Chapter 4

PROBABILITY DISTRIBUTIONS

4.1 DEFINITIONS FOR DISCRETE VARIATES

A specification of the probabilities associated with every point of a sample space is termed a *probability distribution*; it shows how the probability of unity (i.e. certainty) that an event lies in the sample space is distributed between alternative points. If x is the value taken by a discrete variate (e.g. the value shown by a single die, the number of days with frost in January, the number of telephone calls received by an operator in one day), and for each possible value of x the function $f(x)$ is the associated probability, then $f(x)$ is termed the *frequency function* or *probability density function* (p.d.f.). Any p.d.f. must satisfy the conditions that

$$f(x) \text{ is single valued};$$

$$f(x) \geqslant 0, \text{ for all } x \text{ in the sample space}; \qquad (4.1)$$

$$\Sigma f(x) = 1, \text{ for summation over the sample space}. \qquad (4.2)$$

Any function of x that satisfies these three conditions is capable of being a p.d.f. Equation (4.2) is sometimes known as the *honesty condition*.

Similarly, if two variates are required to specify a point in the sample space, and $f(x_1, x_2)$ is the probability that they take values x_1, x_2, then $f(x_1, x_2)$ is the joint p.d.f. In the example of two dice, $f(x_1, x_2)$ must be defined for the 36 combinations of x_1, x_2 represented in Fig. 3.3, where x_i is the value shown by die i. If the dice are well-balanced and fairly thrown,

$$\left.\begin{aligned} f(x_1, x_2) &= \tfrac{1}{36} \quad (1 \leqslant x_1 \leqslant 6, 1 \leqslant x_2 \leqslant 6), \\ &= 0 \quad \text{elsewhere.} \end{aligned}\right\} \qquad (4.3)$$

Here the variates have independent probabilities; each has p.d.f.

$$\left.\begin{aligned} f_0(x) &= \tfrac{1}{6} \quad (1 \leqslant x \leqslant 6), \\ &= 0 \quad \text{elsewhere;} \end{aligned}\right\} \qquad (4.4)$$

27

moreover

$$f(x_1, x_2) = f_0(x_1) \cdot f_0(x_2), \tag{4.5}$$

which is a necessary and sufficient condition for independence (section 3.5). If the dice were not well-balanced, the p.d.f. would not be equal at all the 36 points, but equation (4.5) would still hold if the fall of one die were unaffected by that of the other. Of course the balance of the dice is a purely physical property dependent on careful construction. In practice, none will be perfectly balanced in respect of the six faces, though those used by enthusiastic gamblers are likely either to be nearly balanced or to be deliberately biased! Independence depends much more on the conditions of throwing. Under normal circumstances, an assumption that the two dice have independent probability distributions will be justified by the fact that they are thrown in such a way as not to interfere with one another; if the dice were attached to one another by a short thread, or if before each throw die 2 was placed with the same face upwards as die 1, independence would be destroyed.

The coin and die system of Fig. 3.1 could be discussed similarly, where x_1 can then take only the two values 'H', 'T' (for 'heads' and 'tails'); under well-balanced fair conditions $f(x_1, x_2) = 1/12$.

Of course, for continuous variates, the probability will have to be associated with differential elements of the sample space, and equation (4.2) will be replaced by an integral (section 4.8).

4.2   The Binomial Distribution

Return now to Experiment TWO, or rather to a generalised form of it with N pairs instead of 16, the outcome of each pair being independent of that of all others. Write for any one pair

$$Pr(\alpha) = P \tag{4.6}$$

as in section 3.7, and for convenience define Q by

$$Pr(\delta) = 1 - P = Q. \tag{4.7}$$

The sample space is N-dimensional with 2^N points corresponding to the 2^N possible sequences of N letters every one of which is either α or δ. As already shown for one example in section 3.7, for any one such sequence that contains α exactly r times the multiplication theorem leads to the probability

$$P^r Q^{N-r}. \tag{4.8}$$

For most purposes no particular interest attaches to knowledge of *which* pairs were α but only to the total number of α records. This implies consideration of the single variate r (here r is used as a name for a particular example of a variate, instead of the general symbol x), for which the sample space contains only the values 0, 1, ..., 16, instead of N two-valued variates. The number of possible sequences in which α occurs r times out of N is obviously

$$\binom{N}{r} = \frac{N!}{r!(N-r)!};$$

these are mutually exclusive, each has the probability (4.8), and therefore by a generalisation of equation (3.5) the probability of a specified r is

$$Pr(r) = f(r), \tag{4.9}$$

where

$$\left.\begin{aligned} f(r) &= \binom{N}{r} P^r Q^{N-r} \quad (0 \leqslant r \leqslant N) \\ &= 0 \quad \text{elsewhere.} \end{aligned}\right\} \tag{4.10}$$

This is the p.d.f. for the *binomial probability distribution*, one of the most important distributions for discrete variates. Obviously $f(r)$ satisfies the conditions (4.1), (4.2), since

$$\sum_0^N f(r) = 1.$$

It is applicable to many other situations: the number of heads in throws of N coins, the number of dice showing 3 or more in a set of N, the number of male births in a sequence of N at a maternity hospital, or the number of defective transistors in a factory batch of N. The common feature is that N successive observations are made on a variate that can take only two values, the probabilities for the two alternatives remaining fixed throughout and outcomes of different observations being independent.

4.3 PROBABILITY GENERATING FUNCTION

Suppose that $f(x)$ is the p.d.f. of a discrete variate x. Define the function $G(\alpha)$ by

$$G(\alpha) = \sum f(x) \alpha^x, \tag{4.11}$$

where summation is over the sample space; α is purely a 'dummy' having no quantitative meaning and merely serving to distinguish the terms. This is known as the *probability generating function* (p.g.f.) of x, because it presents the probability of each x as the coefficient of a distinct term, α^x. Often by formal mathematics the right-hand side of (4.11) can be contracted, and certain operations can then be more conveniently executed.

For example, when $f(r)$ has the form of (4.10), the p.g.f. of r is

$$G(\alpha) = \sum_{0}^{N} \binom{N}{r} P^r Q^{N-r} \alpha^r$$

$$= (Q + P\alpha)^N. \tag{4.12}$$

This should make clear why the binomial distribution is so called: the coefficient of α^r in the expansion of the binomial expression (4.12) is the probability that r of the pairs in the generalised Experiment TWO show the result α, and consequently $(N-r)$ pairs show δ.

4.4   THE MEAN

The *mean* of any probability distribution is defined as the arithmetic average of the variate; the possible values must contribute to the average in proportion to the limiting relative frequencies implied by their probabilities. Several alternative notations are useful, but for the present the mean of a variate x will be denoted by

$$E(x) = \sum xf(x), \tag{4.13}$$

summation being over the sample space and $f(x)$ being the p.d.f. By virtue of (4.2), this is the required average.

Comparison of (4.11), (4.13) shows immediately the important result

$$E(x) = \frac{d}{d\alpha} G(\alpha) \Big|_{\alpha=1}. \tag{4.14}$$

For example, the mean of r for the binomial distribution may be obtained from (4.12) as

$$E(r) = NP, \tag{4.15}$$

(A1–A4). The result is scarcely surprising, but the agreement of proof with intuition is satisfactory!

4.5   EXPECTATION

The symbol $E(\ )$ is read as 'the expectation', and is used more generally to refer to the average value of any quantity contained within the ( ). Let $h(x)$ be any single-valued function of x. The general definition is

$$E(h) = \sum h(x)f(x). \tag{4.16}$$

If c is a constant, two obvious results are:

$$E(c) = c, \tag{4.17}$$

and

$$E(ch) = cE(h). \tag{4.18}$$

Also, if $h_1(x)$, $h_2(x)$ are any two single-valued functions,

$$E(h_1 + h_2) = E(h_1) + E(h_2). \tag{4.19}$$

These last three results follow directly from the definition (4.16).

It is important to remember that the expectation function $E(\ )$ always refers to averaging over the probability distribution of the expression placed within $(\ )$. Thus one may require and find an expectation over a bivariate distribution such as that indicated by Fig. 3.3. If $f(x_1, x_2)$ is the probability that the two dice in that example show faces x_1, x_2, then for any single-valued function $h(x_1, x_2)$

$$E(h) = \sum h(x_1, x_2) f(x_1, x_2) \tag{4.20}$$

with summation over all the 36 pairs of x_1, x_2. Again, if t is any statistic (section 3.8) from a set of observations, that is to say any numerical quantity uniquely determined by the observations, $E(t)$ means the average of t taken over all possible observations with relative frequencies equal to the probabilities; sections 9.1, 9.2 contain some non-trivial examples.

4.6 THE VARIANCE

For the binomial distribution, additional results are easily obtained. One at least is of practical importance for indicating the extent to which repetitions of the experiment may differ in the value of r recorded even when P remains constant. Consider

$$E[r(r-1)] = \sum r(r-1) f(r). \tag{4.21}$$

By comparison with (4.11),

$$E[r(r-1)] = \frac{d^2}{d\alpha^2} G(\alpha) \Big|_{\alpha=1}$$

$$= N(N-1)P^2; \tag{4.22}$$

see also (A5–A6). Now one may readily verify that

$$(r - NP)^2 = r(r-1) + r - 2NPr + N^2 P^2, \tag{4.23}$$

and therefore (A7)

$$E[(r-NP)^2] = E[r(r-1)] + E(r) - 2NPE(r) + N^2P^2$$

by (4.18), (4.19), (4.22)

$$= NPQ. \tag{4.24}$$

For any variate, x, a function $h(x)$ might be defined as the square of the deviation of x from $E(x)$, where the expectation has reference to any stated probability distribution for x. Then $E[h(x)]$ is the *mean square deviation* of x, the average (over the distribution of x), of the squared difference between each x and the mean of x; more commonly today, this quantity is known as the *variance* of x (section 4.9). Its use will become clearer later, but even now some intuitive appreciation can be gained.

Equation (4.24) gives the variance of r, the variate in the binomial distribution (4.10). It may be calculated for Experiment TWO, for which $N=16$ and the null hypothesis states $P=\frac{1}{2}$. Hence

$$E(r) = 8,$$

$$E[(r-NP)^2] = 16.\tfrac{1}{2}.\tfrac{1}{2} = 4.$$

Consequently a value of r that deviates by 2 from its expectation would make exactly an average contribution to the variance; hence an experiment that led to the actual record $r_0=10$ would obviously not be very surprising. On the other hand, a value of r deviating by 4 from NP would have $(r_0-NP)^2=16$, and can occur only rarely since frequent occurrence would certainly cause the variance to exceed 4. Similarly a deviation of 6, with $(r_0-NP)^2=36$, must be much rarer. Hence $r_0=4$ or $r_0=12$ would be in some conflict with the null hypothesis, and $r_0=2$ or $r_0=14$ is unlikely to occur if that hypothesis be true. The full argument without use of the variance is presented in section 5.2, but the simple calculations here give a little insight.

4.7 NUMERICAL EXAMPLES

The probability for each value of r for the binomial distribution has been worked out for $N=16$, using both $P=0.5$ and $P=0.75$ (so as to illustrate an unsymmetrical situation.) These are shown in Table 4.1, with corresponding results for $N=8$; they have been calculated from equation (4.10). The probabilities for $N=8$ are shown in Figs. 4.1, 4.2, in a standard form of graphical representation known as a *histogram*. The diagram consists of a horizontal scale marked in sections to correspond to the possible values of r; on each section stands a rectangle whose area is proportional to the probability of that value of r.

TABLE 4.1

Examples of probabilities in the binomial distribution

Probabilities for

No. of successes	$N=8$		$N=16$	
r	$P=0.5$	$P=0.75$	$P=0.5$	$P=0.75$
0	0.0039	0.0000	0.0000	0.0000
1	0.0312	0.0004	0.0003	0.0000
2	0.1094	0.0038	0.0018	0.0000
3	0.2188	0.0231	0.0085	0.0000
4	0.2734	0.0865	0.0278	0.0000
5	0.2188	0.2076	0.0666	0.0003
6	0.1094	0.3115	0.1222	0.0013
7	0.0312	0.2670	0.1746	0.0058
8	0.0039	0.1001	0.1964	0.0197
9	—	—	0.1746	0.0524
10	—	—	0.1222	0.1101
11	—	—	0.0666	0.1802
12	—	—	0.0278	0.2252
13	—	—	0.0085	0.2079
14	—	—	0.0018	0.1336
15	—	—	0.0003	0.0535
16	—	—	0.0000	0.0100
Total	1.0000	1.0000	1.0000	1.0000

4.8 CONTINUOUS VARIATES

If x is a continuous variate, such as those mentioned in section 1.3, the probability density function $f(x)$ must be associated with a differential element; for an infinitesimal value of dx, $f(x)dx$ is the probability that an observation lies between x and $x+dx$. The p.d.f. must be single-valued and must have the two properties suggested by analogy with (4.1), (4.2):

$$f(x) \geqslant 0 \text{ for all } x \text{ in the sample space,} \qquad (4.25)$$

$$\int f(x)\,dx = 1 \text{ for integration over the sample space.} \qquad (4.26)$$

When only one variate is under discussion, the sample space must be either the whole of the linear continuum from $-\infty$ to $+\infty$ or some finite part of this.

When plotted against x, $f(x)$ will represent a curve, which in the more important examples is continuous although continuity is not essential. Fig. 4.3 illustrates this. Introduction of a convention that $f(x)$ is defined to be zero everywhere outside the sample space enables all problems to be discussed as though the space extended from $-\infty$ to $+\infty$, so that (4.26) becomes

$$\int_{-\infty}^{\infty} f(x)\,dx = 1. \qquad (4.27)$$

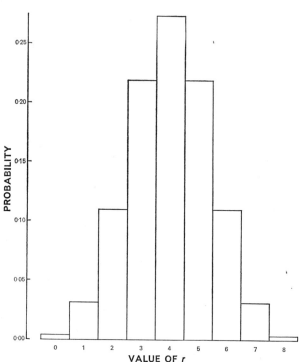

Fig. 4.1. Histogram for binomial distribution with $N=8$, $P=0.5$.

Some variates are necessarily positive, and the convention may then be modified so that the limits are 0, $+\infty$. Note particularly that this kind of convention has no theoretical importance, its sole purpose being to remove the need to state formulae and theorems twice, with infinite and with finite limits. For example, weights of adult men will certainly lie between 20 kg and 300 kg, but to specify exactly the least possible and the greatest possible weight is impracticable. However, agreement to use the interval $(-\infty, +\infty)$ or $(0, +\infty)$ as the sample space, with $f(x)$ equal to zero except within the range of weights that can occur, enables general formulae to be applied without specification of the two extremes.

Fig. 4.3 illustrates such a curve, the vertical scale being so taken as to make (4.27) true. One need not discuss at this stage whether the two 'tails' of the curve meet the x-axis at finite points or are asymptotic to it;

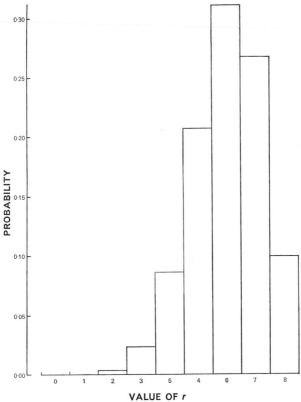

Fig. 4.2. Histogram for binomial distribution with $N=8$, $P=0.75$.

the distinction is of negligible importance outside the range shown. The area between the curve and the x-axis bounded by any two ordinates is the relative frequency with which x occurs in the interval (a, b). That is to say

$$Pr(a < x < b) = \int_a^b f(x)\,dx. \qquad (4.28)$$

The expectation operator can be used also with continuous variates. Analogously to (4.16), for an arbitrary function $h(x)$

$$E(h) = \int_{-\infty}^{\infty} h(x)f(x)\,dx. \qquad (4.29)$$

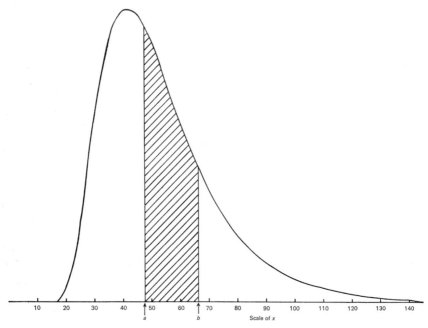

Fig. 4.3. Illustration of a p.d.f., $f(x)$, plotted against x.
The area between the curve and the horizontal axis is made unity.
The shaded area is the probability that a value of x lies between a and b.

The results stated in (4.17)–(4.19) remain true. As an important particular case, the mean of the distribution is

$$E(x) = \int_{-\infty}^{\infty} xf(x)\,dx. \qquad (4.30)$$

For continuous variates, probability generating functions cannot be used, because the notion of a series in which the coefficient of each distinct term is one of the required probabilities is not applicable. A similar facility in handling properties of distributions can be gained from other types of generating function, however.

Again the ideas are readily extended to two or more variates. The example of ages, heights and weights of students mentioned in section 3.2 would use a p.d.f. $f(x_1, x_2, x_3)$, which is a function of three variables, such that

$$f(x_1, x_2, x_3)\, dx_1\, dx_2\, dx_3 \qquad (4.31)$$

represents the probability that the three quantities for a particular student lie within a differential element of the sample space bounded by x_i, $x_i + dx_i$ for $i = 1, 2, 3$. The sample space could be taken as bounded by the limits suggested in section 3.2 or, by definition of the p.d.f. as zero in appropriate regions, the limits can be taken as 0 to $+\infty$ or $-\infty$ to $+\infty$. Obviously (4.27)–(4.30) generalise, though the integrations will sometimes introduce considerable technical difficulties. Most of this book is concerned with univariate distributions.

4.9 MOMENTS

The moments of a probability distribution are a sequence of functions of the parameters uniquely determined by the p.d.f. Moreover, knowledge of the moments serves uniquely to determine the p.d.f., except in certain peculiar and unusual circumstances (a much deeper theorem, which will not be discussed in this book). Of greater practical importance is the fact that the early members of the sequence summarise a great deal of the main features of the character of the p.d.f.

For a continuous variate with $f(x)$ as its p.d.f., the *moment of order* k *about the origin* is defined as

$$\mu'_k \equiv E(x^k) = \int_{-\infty}^{\infty} x^k f(x)\, dx \qquad (4.32)$$

for the positive integers 1, 2, 3, ... In particular, μ'_1 is the mean of the distribution, $E(x)$ and because this quantity is wanted so often it is usually written simply μ.

More commonly used, because they are independent of a simple shift of origin in the scale of x, are the *central moments*, where the central moment of order k is defined as

$$\mu_k \equiv E[(x-\mu)^k] = \int_{-\infty}^{\infty} (x-\mu)^k f(x)\, dx. \qquad (4.33)$$

For a discrete variate, both types of moment are defined with summations in place of integrations; the similarity is so close that (4.34), (4.35), (4.38)–(4.41) below are true for both continuous and discrete variates. Expansion of the binomial term on the right of (4.33) and integration term by term leads to simple relations between central moments and origin-moments (A8–A9), of which

$$\mu_2 = \mu_2' - \mu^2, \tag{4.34}$$

$$\mu_3 = \mu_3' - 3\mu\mu_2' + 2\mu^3 \tag{4.35}$$

are typical. Similarly the μ_k' can be expressed as functions of the μ_k; both sets contain the same information, and for most purposes the central moments are preferred.

The second central moment, μ_2, is the most important single quantity for describing the shape of a probability distribution (the mean of course describes only the position). It is a measure of the dispersion of individual values of the variate about the mean. Under the usual name of *variance*, it has already been introduced in section 4.6, where the formula for the binomial distribution was found to be

$$\mu_2 = NPQ. \tag{4.36}$$

Corresponding formulae will be required also for many other distributions. The physical dimensionality of μ_2 is the square of that of x; the square root of μ_2, measured in the same physical units as x, is termed the *standard deviation* (or S.D.). Populations with identical means may differ widely in variance or standard deviation. For example, individual packages of butter of reputed weight $\frac{1}{4}$ lb each might have mean weight 0·27 lb and S.D. 0·01 lb (the student should think why the mean is likely to exceed 0·25 lb); individual apples in a case might also have mean weight 0·27 lb, but their S.D. could be much greater, say 0·06 lb.

Suppose that the curve of $f(x)$ plotted against x is symmetrical about an ordinate. Evidently this ordinate must be at the mean, μ, and for all a

$$f(\mu - a) = f(\mu + a). \tag{4.37}$$

Inspection of (4.33) then shows that all central moments of odd order are zero. Hence μ_3, μ_5, ..., are measures of departure from symmetry. The moments of even order, in complicated fashion, are measures of the type of 'peakedness' of the curve of $f(x)$ against x.

4.10   MOMENT GENERATING FUNCTION

A generating function of great importance for continuous and discrete variates is one in which moments appear as the coefficients of successive terms. Define the *moment generating function* (m.g.f.) by

$$M_x(\theta) \equiv E(e^{\theta x}), \tag{4.38}$$

where θ is a dummy, as was α in (4.11). Then, provided that the integral or the sum exists (and existence for small θ suffices for this purpose), the expression of $M_x(\theta)$ as a power series in θ will have μ'_k as the coefficient of $\theta^k/k!$ (A10). More general results follow by taking $h(x)$ as an arbitrary single-valued function of x and defining $M_{h(x)}(\theta)$, or simply $M_h(\theta)$, by

$$M_h(\theta) = E[e^{\theta h(x)}]. \tag{4.39}$$

Consideration of the functions $h(x)+c$ and $ch(x)$, where c is a constant, leads to

$$M_{h+c}(\theta) = E[e^{c\theta} e^{\theta h(x)}]$$
$$= e^{c\theta} M_h(\theta), \tag{4.40}$$

and

$$M_{ch}(\theta) = E[e^{c\theta h(x)}]$$
$$= M_h(c\theta). \tag{4.41}$$

By taking $h(x)=x$, $c=-\mu$, equation (4.40) gives a relation between the moment generating function for central moments and that for origin-moments:

$$M_{x-\mu}(\theta) = e^{-\mu\theta} M_x(\theta). \tag{4.42}$$

When expanded in powers of θ, the coefficient of $\theta^k/k!$ on the left-hand side of (4.42) must be μ_k, as is obvious from (4.33), (4.39); consequently, evaluation of the product of the two infinite series on the right-hand side yields relations such as (4.34), (4.35) by equating coefficients of corresponding powers.

When x has a distribution for which a p.g.f. exists, comparison of (4.11), (4.38) shows that $M_x(\theta)$ is obtainable by substitution of e^θ for α in $G(\alpha)$, the p.g.f. For example, from (4.12), the m.g.f. for the binomial distribution is

$$M_x(\theta) = (Q+Pe^\theta)^N. \tag{4.43}$$

4.11 An Important Distribution

For several reasons, some of which will appear later, the most important of all distributions of continuous variates is one which has the form

$$f(x) = K\exp\left[-\frac{(x-\xi)^2}{2\sigma^2}\right]. \tag{4.44}$$

In this chapter, it will be used simply to illustrate some of the results achieved so far. Evidently $f(x)$ satisfies (4.25) for all x; if the integral from $-\infty$ to $+\infty$ has a finite value, as is intuitively likely from the form of the integrand, suitable choice of K will ensure that (4.26) is also satisfied. Integration (A11–A17) leads to

$$\int_{-\infty}^{\infty} f(x)\,dx = K\sigma\sqrt{(2\pi)},\tag{4.45}$$

and therefore the necessary and sufficient condition for (4.44) to be a p.d.f. is

$$K = 1/\sigma\sqrt{(2\pi)}.\tag{4.46}$$

For this p.d.f., the mean, variance and higher moments can be found by direct evaluation of (4.32); for every k, one or more steps of integrating by parts reduces the integrand either to a multiple of $f(x)$ or to a multiple of $(x-\xi)f(x)$. However, the moment generating function enables the whole thing to be done more neatly. For the m.g.f., using (A18), (A19),

$$M_x(\theta) = K \int_{-\infty}^{\infty} \exp\left[x\theta - \frac{(x-\xi)^2}{2\sigma^2}\right] dx$$

$$= \exp[\xi\theta + \tfrac{1}{2}\sigma^2\,\theta^2].\tag{4.47}$$

Expansion in powers of θ obviously gives ξ as the coefficient of the first power; hence

$$\mu = \mu_1' = \xi.\tag{4.48}$$

Then by use of (4.42), the m.g.f. for central moments is

$$M_{x-\mu}(\theta) = e^{\frac{1}{2}\sigma^2\theta^2}.\tag{4.49}$$

Evidently the expansion of this will have only even powers of θ, so that all central moments of odd degree are zero; the distribution is symmetrical (cf. section 4.9). Moreover, the coefficient of $\theta^2/2!$ is σ^2, and therefore

$$\mu_2 = \sigma^2.\tag{4.50}$$

The general result is easily obtained; the term in θ^{2j} in (4.49) is

$$\frac{\sigma^{2j}\,\theta^{2j}}{2^j\,j!} = \frac{2j!\,\sigma^{2j}}{2^j\,j!}\cdot\frac{\theta^{2j}}{2j!}$$

and therefore

$$\mu_{2j} = \frac{2j!\,\sigma^{2j}}{2^j\,j!}\tag{4.51}$$

for any integer j.

*4.12 A METHOD OF FINDING PARTICULAR MOMENTS

Note that, if $M_x(\theta)$ is known, μ_k' can be found by differentiating this m.g.f. k times with respect to θ and then equating θ to zero; see (A20), (A21). This method is frequently useful. For example, from (4.47)

$$\frac{dM}{d\theta} = (\xi + \sigma^2\theta)M,$$

and

$$\frac{d^2M}{d\theta^2} = \sigma^2 M + (\xi + \sigma^2\theta)^2 M.$$

Since $\theta = 0$ gives $M = 1$,

$$\mu_1' = \xi, \tag{4.52}$$

$$\mu_2' = \sigma^2 + \xi^2, \tag{4.53}$$

and (4.34) gives

$$\mu_2 = \sigma^2. \tag{4.50}$$

The same method gives μ_k from $M_{x-\mu}(\theta)$.

EXERCISES

4.1 A game of chance is so organised that in one trial a player can gain any integer number of points, 0, 1, 2, ..., r, ... The probability that he gains r points is

$$f(r) = \binom{w+r-1}{r}\alpha^w(1-\alpha)^r,$$

where the integer w is known and α is an unknown parameter $(0 < \alpha < 1)$. Prove that $f(r)$ satisfies the necessary and sufficient conditions for being a frequency function. Prove that

$$E\left(\frac{w-1}{w+r-1}\right) = \alpha.$$

Find also

$$E\left(\frac{w+r}{w}\right).$$

4.2 A variate has p.d.f.

$$f(x) = A \text{ for } -1 \leqslant x \leqslant 4 \quad (A \text{ is a constant})$$

$$= 0 \quad \text{elsewhere.}$$

Find A. Determine the moment generating function and from it obtain the mean and μ_2, μ_3, the second and third moments about the mean.

4.3 The discrete variate r has the p.d.f.

$$f(r) = e^{-a} a^r / r! \quad (r = 0, 1, 2, \ldots).$$

Find the moment generating function of r. By differentiating $M(\theta)$ with respect to θ twice, and putting $\theta = 0$ in $M'(\theta)$ and $M''(\theta)$, prove that the mean and variance of the distribution are both equal to a. Also find $E(r)$ and $E[r(r-1)]$ by procedures similar to those of section 4.6, and verify these results.

4.4 (More difficult; summation of infinite series needed). A, B, C in order throw a die. If A throws 5 or 6, he wins; failing that, if B throws an even number he wins; failing that, if C throws an odd number he wins. If all fail, the turn goes back to A and play continues. Find the probability (i) that A eventually wins, (ii) that B eventually wins, (iii) that A has at least three turns.

4.5 Write out formal proofs of (4.17), (4.18), (4.19).

4.6 For the sample space of Fig. 3.3, if the dice show faces x_1, x_2, find $E(x_1)$, $E(x_1^2)$, $E(x_1 \times x_2)$, and $E(x_1^2 x_2)$

(i) when both dice are well-balanced and independently and fairly thrown;

(ii) when the probabilities of 1, 2, 3, 4, 5, 6 are 3/20, 3/20, 3/20, 3/20, 3/20, 1/4 for die 1, and 1/12, 1/6, 1/6, 1/6, 1/6, 1/4 for die 2, and the two dice are thrown independently.

4.7 Repeat the calculations of Exercise 4.6 when the probability distribution of x_1, x_2 is specified by

$$f(x_1, x_2) = 1/11(x_1 + x_2 - 1) \quad \text{if } x_1 + x_2 \leqslant 7,$$
$$= 1/11(13 - x_1 - x_2) \quad \text{if } x_1 + x_2 \geqslant 7.$$

Show diagrammatically the probability for each point of the sample space, and verify (section 4.1) that $f(x_1, x_2)$ is a p.d.f.

4.8 Write out a formal proof that, if (4.37) is true, $\mu_k = 0$ for all *odd* integers k.

4.9 Write $U_2 = E[(x - X)^2]$ for an arbitrary fixed X. Prove that the minimum of U_2 with respect to X occurs at $X = \mu$, both for a discrete and for a continuous distribution of x.

4.10 Evaluate the product of two series on the right-hand side of (4.42) in order to verify (4.34), (4.35), and to find μ_4 in similar form.

4.11 Use (4.43) to find μ_2, μ_3, μ_4 for the binomial distribution as functions of N, P.

4.12 The variate x has an arbitrary probability distribution (discrete or continuous). Explain carefully why it is not in general true that

$$E(x^2) = [E(x)]^2$$

or

$$E(x^{-1}) = 1/E(x).$$

Illustrate by means of situations discussed in this chapter and by reference to Exercise 4.1, but concentrate on giving a clear explanation rather than a succession of mathematical equations. Can you devise examples of distributions for which either or both of these equations is true?

4.13 Cubes are manufactured in such a way that the length of side has p.d.f.

$$f(x) = 1 \quad \text{for } 1 \leqslant x \leqslant 2$$
$$= 0 \quad \text{elsewhere.}$$

Find the mean and standard deviation for the distribution of volume (each article is a perfect cube, the variation in dimensions being only from cube to cube).

Chapter 5

PROPERTIES AND USES OF DISTRIBUTIONS

5.1 THE DISTRIBUTION FUNCTION

Interest often lies in the total probability that a variate exceeds a specified value. Indeed, as already suggested in sections 3.1, 4.6, this is the kind of probability used in tests of statistical significance. The reason is apparent when large numbers of observations are considered. Suppose that the null hypothesis of section 3.1 were applied to an experiment with 1000 pairs of rats. The probability that exactly 500 pairs are recorded as α is, by (4.10),

$$\frac{1000!}{500!\,500!} \cdot 2^{-1000}. \tag{5.1}$$

This is an exceedingly small amount, as may be verified by use of Stirling's formula (A22). The same numerical value is the probability of obtaining exactly 500 heads in 1000 spins of a perfectly balanced coin. Yet such a result would certainly not be interpreted as evidence that the null hypothesis in section 3.1 was false or that the coin was ill-balanced.

Whenever the number of alternative possible results is large, the position may be that each one of them has a very small probability. The evidence against a null hypothesis is best assessed in terms of the probability of a result *at least as extreme* as that observed. In the example above, the probability of 506 α-pairs is

$$\frac{1000!}{506!\,494!} 2^{-1000}, \tag{5.2}$$

numerically somewhat smaller than that for 500 α-pairs. However, the probability of observing *at least* 506 α-pairs is, by (3.5) since the alternative numbers are mutually exclusive, the sum of expressions of this kind based upon 506, 507, 508, ..., 999, 1000 in turn; this can be shown to be very much larger, in fact of the order of 0·35.

44

Argument along these lines involves the *distribution function*. If $f(x)$ is the probability that a discrete variate takes the value x, the distribution function is defined as

$$F(X) = \sum_{x \leqslant X} f(x), \tag{5.3}$$

the total probability that x is less than or equal to a specified X. In the common case in which the sample space for x is some or all of the positive integers,

$$F(X) = \sum_{x=0}^{X} f(x). \tag{5.4}$$

Similarly, if $f(x)$ is the p.d.f. of a continuous variate, the distribution function is defined as

$$F(X) = \int_{-\infty}^{X} f(x)\,dx. \tag{5.5}$$

The function $F(X)$ is a monotonically increasing function of x, whose value must attain or asymptotically approach limits of 0 and 1 for small and large X respectively. For discrete x, $F(X)$ is a step function looking like that in Fig. 5.1; for a continuous x, it is a continuous curve such as that in Fig. 5.2.

5.2   A TEST OF SIGNIFICANCE

If Experiment TWO is to be discussed in relation to the null hypothesis stated in section 3.1 and expressed by equation (3.1), no interest will attach to the particular order of α and δ in the records but only to the total number of times that α occurs (section 4.2). The test of significance will require reference to the distribution function of r,

$$F(R) = 2^{-N} \sum_{r=0}^{R} \binom{16}{r}. \tag{5.4a}$$

This is readily obtained by summations of the appropriate probabilities in the third series of Table 4.1. For comparison with that table, all the four distribution functions obtainable from it have been calculated and are presented in Table 5.1. The general formula,

$$F(R) = \sum_{r=0}^{R} \binom{N}{r} P^r (1-P)^{N-r}, \tag{5.4b}$$

reduces to (5.4a) when $P = \tfrac{1}{2}$, $N = 16$.

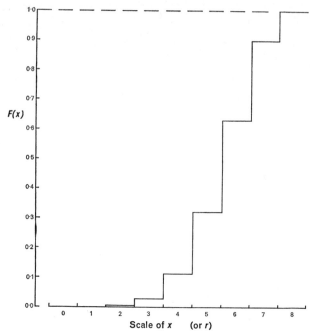

Fig. 5.1. Illustration of a distribution function for a discrete variate that takes only positive integer values (cf. Fig. 4.2. and Table 5.1).

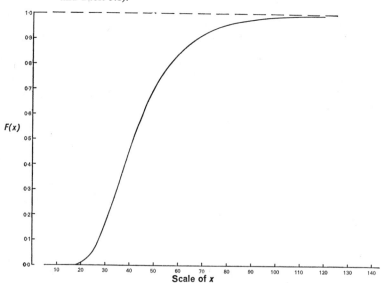

Fig. 5.2. Illustration of distribution function for a continuous variate.

TABLE 5.1

Four examples of distribution functions for the binomial distribution

Values of R	$N=8$		$N=16$	
	$P=0{\cdot}5$	$P=0{\cdot}75$	$P=0{\cdot}5$	$P=0{\cdot}75$
0	0·0039	0·0000	0·0000	0·0000
1	0·0352	0·0004	0·0003	0·0000
2	0·1445	0·0042	0·0021	0·0000
3	0·3633	0·0273	0·0106	0·0000
4	0·6367	0·1138	0·0384	0·0000
5	0·8555	0·3215	0·1051	0·0003
6	0·9648	0·6329	0·2272	0·0016
7	0·9961	0·8999	0·4018	0·0075
8	1·0000	1·0000	0·5982	0·0271
9	—	—	0·7728	0·0796
10	—	—	0·8949	0·1896
11	—	—	0·9616	0·3698
12	—	—	0·9894	0·5950
13	—	—	0·9979	0·8029
14	—	—	0·9997	0·9365
15	—	—	1·0000	0·9900
16	—	—	1·0000	1·0000

The general logical argument underlying a test of statistical significance should now be studied carefully, after which the problem under discussion will provide a simple illustration. The user of the test states a null hypothesis, a statement (about one or more parameters of his experiment) that he wishes to be able to reject if his experiment provides convincing evidence. He also chooses a small probability, commonly known as the *significance level*, as the risk he is prepared to take that his rule will lead him to reject a null hypothesis that is true. This point he should reach before the experiment is performed. After he has the experimental results, he examines some statistic whose expectation if the null hypothesis be true he can calculate, and which will tend to deviate from this expectation to an increasing extent the more markedly that hypothesis is untrue. He then looks at the actual deviation of the particular value of the statistic in his experiment; if on the basis of the null hypothesis the probability that so large a deviation occurs by chance is less than the significance level, he rejects the null hypothesis. Thus he argues that his data, although perhaps not totally inconsistent with the null hypothesis, are so extreme as to be most unlikely to have occurred if that hypothesis were true. On the other hand, if the probability is not less than the significance level, he does not reject the null hypothesis; as examples will show, this is in no way equivalent to proving the hypothesis to be true.

As already explained, if the only data obtained from Experiment TWO are the records of α and δ, equation (3.1) is the appropriate null hypothesis. There is a long tradition of using 0·05 as the significance level; the investigator has full liberty to choose differently and he should make a conscious choice of the risk he will take, but 0·05 will serve for this exposition. After conducting the experiment, he can compare the number of α-records with the distribution function calculated from the null hypothesis. If r_0 is the number in the actual experiment, the probability that this or any greater number should occur may be written

$$Pr(r \geqslant r_0) = 1 - F(r_0 - 1), \qquad (5.6)$$

as should be obvious from the definition of $F(R)$ in (5.4a), (5.4b).

Suppose that $r_0 = 14$ had been found. Using the penultimate column of Table 5.1, equation (5.6) gives

$$Pr(r \geqslant r_0) = 1 - F(13)$$
$$= 0 \cdot 0021, \qquad (5.7)$$

which is smaller than 0·05. The data are said to show a *statistically significant* deviation from the null hypothesis, the number of α-records being large relative to the expectation $(NP = 8)$. On the hypothesis, data as extreme as these would be very rare, and the investigator rejects the hypothesis. The assertion that the oxygen uptake by red blood corpuscles is not affected by treatment A (as compared with D) is untenable; there is clear evidence that, under the conditions of the experiment, rats receiving treatment A will show an increased rate of oxygen uptake.

Suppose instead that $r_0 = 12$ had been found. Then

$$Pr(r \geqslant r_0) = 0 \cdot 0384, \qquad (5.8)$$

still less than 0·05; the conclusion is the same, though the weight of evidence for it is less.

On the other hand, suppose $r_0 = 11$; then

$$Pr(r \geqslant r_0) = 0 \cdot 1051. \qquad (5.9)$$

Even if the null hypothesis is true, an excess of α-records as great as this would occur on average about once in ten experiments; the evidence is not such as to justify rejection of that hypothesis. Note, however, that many other hypotheses also would not be rejected by a test at the same significance level. For example, $Pr(\alpha)=0\cdot489$, or $Pr(\alpha)=0\cdot543$ would certainly not be rejected; although these and many other hypotheses are perhaps less intrinsically interesting than that corresponding to the statement that A and D do not differ in effect, they serve to demonstrate that $r_0=11$ certainly does not prove the truth of $Pr(\alpha)=\frac{1}{2}$. Even $r_0=8$ would not prove this (cf. section 6.6).

5.3   EXAMPLES OF DISTRIBUTION FUNCTIONS

For a continuous variate, the distribution function may sometimes be simply expressed. Consider the p.d.f.

$$f(x) = \beta e^{-\beta x} \quad \text{for } x \geqslant 0 \atop = 0 \qquad \text{for } x < 0 \Bigg\} . \qquad (5.10)$$

Then from equation (5.3)

$$F(X) = 1 - e^{-\beta X} \quad \text{for } X \geqslant 0 \atop = 0 \qquad \text{for } X < 0 \Bigg\} . \qquad (5.11)$$

Evidently

$$F(X) \to 1 \text{ as } X \to \infty$$

and, for any X, if β is known $F(X)$ can be read directly from a table of exponentials.

In section 4.11, an important p.d.f. dependent upon two parameters (ξ and σ) was introduced:

$$f(x) = \frac{1}{\sigma\sqrt{(2\pi)}} \exp\left[-\frac{(x-\xi)^2}{2\sigma^2}\right]. \qquad (5.12)$$

Equation (5.5), with the aid of the transformation

$$x = \xi + \sigma t, \qquad (5.13)$$

leads to

$$F(X) = \int_{-\infty}^{(X-\xi)/\sigma} \frac{1}{\sqrt{(2\pi)}} e^{-\frac{1}{2}t^2} dt. \qquad (5.14)$$

This integral cannot be evaluated analytically, but it is of such importance in many statistical operations that very extensive tables have been calculated by numerical integration. As $X \to -\infty$, $F(x)$ is clearly asymptotic to 0, and as $x \to +\infty$ the results (4.45), (4.46) indicate asymptotic approach to 1. Moreover, considerations of symmetry show that

$$F(\xi) = 0\cdot5.$$

Table 5.2 shows a few values; there is no particular theoretical interest in the manner of obtaining them, but the reader should be aware that far more detailed tables exist and some use of these will be made later.

TABLE 5.2

$$\text{Some values of } F(T) = \int_{-\infty}^{T} \frac{1}{\sqrt{(2\pi)}} e^{-\frac{1}{2}t^2} dt$$

T	-2.0	-1.0	0.0	0.5	1.0
$F(T)$	0·023	0·159	0·500	0·691	0·841

T	1.5	1.645	2.0	2.5	3.0
$F(T)$	0·933	0·950	0·977	0·9938	0·9987

5.4   SUMS OF INDEPENDENT OBSERVATIONS

A great amount of statistical theory is concerned with the relation between probability distributions of variates and distributions of functions of these variates. Knowledge of the relative frequency with which alternative values of x will occur implies knowledge of corresponding relative frequencies for e^x, $\sin[x/(1+x^2)]$, or any other single-valued function of x. Mathematical discussion of these may involve fairly trivial transformations of an integrand or of a p.d.f., or may be more complicated. In one sense, the binomial distribution has already given an example of this. Suppose that a variate can take only the values 0, 1, and

$$Pr(y = 1) = P. \tag{5.15}$$

Then if y is observed N times independently, the sum of the observations is equal to the number of times that $y=1$, say r. Comparison with section 4.2 shows that r is exactly as there described for the binomial distribution; hence the distribution found for r is the distribution of the sum of N independently observed variates each distributed like y. Of course, the distribution of y can itself be regarded as a particular case of the binomial, with $N=1$.

A somewhat different simple example can be found in section 5.3, where the relation between a particular distribution of x and the distribution of a linear function of x, given by (5.13), was studied:

$$t = (x-\xi)/\sigma. \tag{5.16}$$

When distributions of two or more variates have been specified, questions may be raised about the distribution of some function of all of them. One of the simplest and most important functions to be considered is the sum of the variates. Suppose that x_1, x_2 are two variates, discrete or continuous, having $f(x_1, x_2)$ as their joint p.d.f. Write

$$u = x_1 + x_2. \tag{5.17}$$

Then by (4.19)

$$E(u) = E(x_1) + E(x_2), \tag{5.18}$$

as is obvious from definitions (A23). More generally, if $x_1, x_2, ..., x_n$ are n distinct variates, the result becomes

$$E\left(\sum_1^n x_i\right) = \sum_1^n E(x_i). \tag{5.19}$$

Equations (5.18), (5.19) are true whatever the form of the p.d.f. More extensive results can be obtained if the variates are independent (section 3.5). For two variates, the necessary and sufficient condition for independence is

$$f(x_1, x_2) = f_1(x_1) . f_2(x_2), \tag{5.20}$$

the expression of (3.8) in terms of p.d.f.'s for discrete or for continuous variates; $f_i(x_i)$ is the p.d.f. of x_i. With u as in (5.17), the m.g.f. of u is

$$M_u(\theta) = E[e^{\theta(x_1 + x_2)}]$$

$$= \int\int e^{\theta(x_1 + x_2)} f_1(x_1) f_2(x_2) \, dx_1 \, dx_2$$

$$= \int e^{\theta x_1} f_1(x_1) \, dx_1 . \int e^{\theta x_2} f_2(x_2) \, dx_2$$

$$= M_{x_1}(\theta) . M_{x_2}(\theta), \tag{5.21}$$

where $M_{x_i}(\theta)$ is the m.g.f. of x_i. A parallel proof shows the result to be true for discrete variates. Again the generalisation is obvious. If the n independent variates x_i have p.d.f.'s $f_i(x_i)$ and $\sum$ denotes summation from 1 to n,

$$M_{\sum x_i}(\theta) = M_{x_1}(\theta) . M_{x_2}(\theta) ... M_{x_n}(\theta). \tag{5.22}$$

An even more general result, following the generalisation from (4.38) to (4.39), has a function $h_i(x_i)$ of x_i replacing each x_i in (5.22).

5.5 Totals and Means of Samples

In section 5.4, the n variates x_i have been introduced as coming from n distinct distributions. A particular case is that of all the distributions being identical, and this in turn is logically equivalent to having n independent observations from one distribution. At the beginning of section 5.4, the variate in a binomial distribution was related in this fashion to the variate y defined in (5.14). As another example, if x represents the number of 'spots' shown at one throw of a cubical die, the properties of x_1, x_2, ..., x_n recorded in n successive independent throws of one die will be the same as if each comes from a different member of a set of n identical dice. Again suppose that x is the height in cm of a student chosen at random (by lot) from all on the rolls of a certain University on 1 November 1968. If 20 successive selections are made independently, it is immaterial whether x_{13} is regarded as the value obtained from the distribution on occasion 13 or as the thirteenth member of a sample of 20 from one distribution. The independence of selection implies a new drawing by lot for each of the values of x_i; to select one student by lot and to include also the 19 names following his in a register would destroy the independence, and might well give 20 students from the Department of Agriculture, or 20 whose names begin 'Mac', on account of the system of constructing the register. In order that x shall have the same distribution throughout the sampling, the complete register must be retained as the frame for selection each time, so that one student may be chosen more than once; if the restriction is introduced that no student can be selected more than once, the p.d.f. for selection of x_2 will differ from that for selection from x_1, although in practice the difference is likely to be negligible for a sample of $n=20$ out of a university containing say 4000 students.

For x_i ($i=1$, 2, ..., n) identically and independently distributed, and therefore having identical m.g.f.'s, equation (5.22) becomes

$$M_{\Sigma x_i}(\theta) = [M_x(\theta)]^n, \tag{5.23}$$

where Σ again denotes summation from 1 to n and $M_x(\theta)$ is the m.g.f. for a single observation on an x_i. Suppose now the mean, $\bar{x}$, of the sample of n is to be studied, where by definition

$$\bar{x} = \Sigma x_i/n. \tag{5.24}$$

The quantity $\bar{x}$ itself has a probability distribution. Every point in the n-dimensional sample space for x_1, x_2, ..., x_n has $\bar{x}$ as a single-valued function of its co-ordinates; in general, however, a particular value of $\bar{x}$ will arise from more than one combination of values of the x_i (e.g. $\bar{x}=2$ or $\bar{x}=3\cdot5$ in Fig. 3.3; in this sample space, $\bar{x}=1$ and $\bar{x}=6$ can arise in only one way), and the probabilities associated with all appropriate values of x_1, x_2, ..., x_n must be summed or integrated to give the probability attaching to this $\bar{x}$. Sometimes the theory of the m.g.f. provides a method of achieving the result more expeditiously than by direct summation or integration. The m.g.f. of $\bar{x}$ is immediately derivable from (5.22), (5.23), by writing $c = 1/n$ in (4.41):

$$M_{\bar{x}}(\theta) = \left[M_x\left(\frac{\theta}{n}\right) \right]^n. \tag{5.25}$$

Equation (5.25) completely specifies the moments of $\bar{x}$ in terms of those of x. If $\bar{\mu}'_k$ is written for the moment of order k of $\bar{x}$ about the origin, equation of coefficients of powers of θ in the expansions of the two sides of (5.25) gives the results. Consideration of the first degree terms alone in

$$1 + \bar{\mu}'_1 \theta + \dots = \left[1 + \mu'_1 \frac{\theta}{n} + \dots \right]^n$$

gives $\hspace{3cm} \bar{\mu}'_1 = \mu'_1; \tag{5.26}$

the mean of the distribution of $\bar{x}$ is equal to that of the distribution of x, perhaps scarcely a surprising result!

This is merely the preliminary to more interesting findings. Write μ for μ'_1, and consider central moments (section 4.9) for x and $\bar{x}$. With the aid of (4.42) if the conclusion is not otherwise obvious, equation (5.25) readily gives

$$M_{\bar{x}-\mu}(\theta) = \left[M_{x-\mu}\left(\frac{\theta}{n}\right) \right]^n. \tag{5.27}$$

This may be written in terms of infinite series (cf. A10):

$$1 + \bar{\mu}_2 \frac{\theta^2}{2!} + \bar{\mu}_3 \frac{\theta^3}{3!} + \bar{\mu}_4 \frac{\theta^4}{4!} + \dots = \left[1 + \mu_2 \frac{\theta^2}{n^2 2!} + \mu_3 \frac{\theta^3}{n^3 3!} + \mu_4 \frac{\theta^4}{n^4 4!} + \dots \right]^n$$

and thence as shown in (A24)

$$= 1 + \frac{\mu_2}{n} \frac{\theta^2}{2!} + \frac{\mu_3}{n^2} \frac{\theta^3}{3!}$$

$$+ \left[\frac{\mu_4}{n^3} + \frac{3(n-1)\mu_2^2}{n^3} \right] \frac{\theta^4}{4!} + \dots.$$

Equation of coefficients of powers of θ then shows that

$$\bar{\mu}_2 = \mu_2/n, \tag{5.28}$$

$$\bar{\mu}_3 = \mu_3/n^2, \tag{5.29}$$

$$\bar{\mu}_4 = [\mu_4 + 3(n-1)\mu_2^2]/n^3, \tag{5.30}$$

and as many additional values as one cares to take the trouble to evaluate. These findings are by no means trivial. All are important, and that for $\bar{\mu}_2$ will be wanted often.

3

5.6 DERIVED DISTRIBUTIONS

The two previous sections have illustrated the process of obtaining the m.g.f. of a variate defined as a function of one or more other variates. Not every probability distribution has a m.g.f.: the sum or integral implied by (4.38) may fail to converge. However, if the m.g.f. exists, the m.g.f. of a sum or mean of a sample of n independent values from the distribution is uniquely determinable. Moreover, the relation between a probability distribution and its m.g.f. is unique, except for certain situations that belong to the 'pathology' of mathematics! From the m.g.f. of the sum or mean, it may therefore be possible to find the uniquely corresponding p.d.f., so completing the cycle.

This method, sometimes applicable to the study of functions other than sums and means, is a powerful technique for the study of distributions derived from that of x. Two important examples follow, and section 9.5 contains another.

5.7 THE POISSON DISTRIBUTION

A distribution of a discrete variate that is commonly associated with the name of the mathematician Poisson arises in various ways. One is as a limiting form of the binomial distribution by allowing P to tend to zero while N increases without limit, yet holding constant the mean

$$\mu = NP. \tag{5.31}$$

Introducing μ from (5.31), equation (4.12) becomes

$$G(\alpha) = \left[1 - \frac{\mu(1-\alpha)}{N}\right]^{N}; \tag{5.32}$$

this is immediately recognisable as an expression with a familiar exponential limit as $N \to \infty$. Hence the p.g.f. for the Poisson distribution is

$$G(\alpha) = e^{-\mu(1-\alpha)}$$

$$= e^{-\mu}e^{\mu\alpha}. \tag{5.33}$$

Expansion as a power series in α gives $Pr(r)$ as the coefficient of α^{r}:

$$Pr(r) = e^{-\mu}\mu^{r}/r! \quad \text{for } r \geqslant 0, \tag{5.34}$$

defining the probability of the variate taking the value 0 or any positive integer. That this p.d.f. satisfies the conditions of section 4.1 ought to be apparent from the fact of it being obtained as a limit from another p.d.f.; more directly, equation (4.2) may be verified as

$$\sum_0^\infty Pr(r) = e^{-\mu} \sum_0^r \frac{\mu^r}{r!}$$

$$= e^{-\mu} . e^{\mu}$$

$$= 1.$$

As explained at the end of section 4.10, the m.g.f. for this distribution is derivable from (5.33), and is

$$M_x(\theta) = \exp[\mu(e^\theta - 1)]. \tag{5.35}$$

Expansion gives, by (A25–A27),

$$M_x(\theta) = 1 + \mu\theta + (\mu + \mu^2)\frac{\theta^2}{2!} + (\mu + 3\mu^2 + \mu^3)\frac{\theta^3}{3!} + \dots. \tag{5.36}$$

Hence the mean is μ, as might be expected. Also

$$\mu_2' = \mu + \mu^2, \tag{5.37}$$

and, by (4.34),

$$\mu_2 = \mu. \tag{5.38}$$

Similarly from (5.34),

$$\mu_3' = \mu + 3\mu^2 + \mu^3. \tag{5.39}$$

Hence, by (4.35),

$$\mu_3 = \mu + 3\mu^2 + \mu^3 - 3\mu(\mu + \mu^2) + 2\mu^3$$

$$= \mu. \tag{5.40}$$

Higher order moments can be found; they are not all equal to μ.

If the variate x_i follows the Poisson distribution defined by (5.33) or (5.34) with $\mu = \xi_i (i = 1, 2, \dots, n)$, then from (5.22), (5.35), and with independent observations on each x_i

$$M_{\Sigma x_i}(\theta) = \exp[(e^\theta - 1) \Sigma \xi_i], \tag{5.41}$$

where again Σ denotes summation from 1 to n. This is recognisable as the m.g.f. of a Poisson distribution in which $\mu = \Sigma \xi_i$. The sum of independent variates from Poisson distributions therefore also has a Poisson distribution in which the parameter is the sum of the separate parameters. If all the ξ_i were equal, the distribution of Σx_i would be Poisson with parameter $n\xi$.

5.8 The Normal or Gaussian Distribution

The distribution introduced in section 4.11 is commonly called the *normal distribution*, less commonly the *Gaussian* in reference to Gauss who made great use of it although it was known before his time. The word 'normal' is used in a special sense, not to be regarded as contrasting with 'abnormal', and for emphasis it will hereafter be given an initial capital: 'Normal'. The general form of the Normal distribution has its p.d.f.,

$$f(x) = \frac{1}{\sigma\sqrt{(2\pi)}} e^{-(x-\xi)^2/2\sigma^2}, \tag{5.42}$$

fully determined by its two parameters ξ, σ^2, and will be briefly referred to as the distribution $N(\xi, \sigma^2)$.

Suppose that the variate x_i has the distribution $N(\xi_i, \sigma_i^2)$, for $i = 1, 2, \ldots, n$, and that the distributions are independent of one another. What is the distribution of $\sum x_i$? That is to say, if one value of the variate is taken from each of the n distributions and the sum of these formed, what can be said about the relative frequencies of different values for this sum when the whole process of selecting the x_i is repeated? From (4.47), (5.22),

$$M_{\sum x_i}(\theta) = \exp(\theta \sum \xi_i + \tfrac{1}{2}\theta^2 \sum \sigma_i^2), \tag{5.43}$$

again using $\sum$ to denote summation from 1 to n. This m.g.f. is of the same form as (4.47), and, because of the unique relation between m.g.f. and p.d.f., there follows the important conclusion that $\sum x_i$ must also be Normally distributed, $N(\sum \xi_i, \sum \sigma_i^2)$.

Next suppose that for all i

$$\left.\begin{array}{r} \xi_i = \xi \\ \sigma_i^2 = \sigma^2 \end{array}\right\}, \tag{5.44}$$

so that all x_i are selected independently from the same distribution, $N(\xi, \sigma^2)$. By particularising (5.43), or directly from (5.23),

$$M_{\sum x_i}(\theta) = \exp(n\xi\theta + \tfrac{1}{2}n\sigma^2 \theta^2), \tag{5.45}$$

so that $\sum x_i$ has the distribution $N(n\xi, n\sigma^2)$. Moreover, for the sample mean defined in (5.24),

$$M_{\bar{x}}(\theta) = \exp(\xi\theta + \sigma^2 \theta^2/2n) \tag{5.46}$$

by (5.25). Comparison with (4.47) shows $\bar{x}$ to have the distribution $N(\xi, \sigma^2/n)$.

Thus totals and means of samples from a Normal distribution are themselves Normally distributed, with parameters obtained from those of the original distribution by rules stated above. Note that for the Poisson distribution the total of independent observations follows a Poisson distribution, but the mean does not. Why?

Despite the examples given in sections 5.7, 5.8, it is not in general true that the sum of independent observations from a distribution follows a distribution of the same kind.

EXERCISES

5.1 Meterological records for the town of A show that between May and September on average one day in three has some rain. Assuming the binomial distribution to be appropriate, calculate probabilities of 0, 1, 2, ..., 7 days without rain during the first 7 days of August. What is the probability of *at least* 3 fine days? Explain why calculations based upon the binomial distribution are likely to be misleading in the real problem.

5.2 The variate x has the p.d.f.
$$f(x) = a \quad \text{for } 0 \leqslant x \leqslant 1/a$$
$$= 0 \quad \text{for other } x.$$
Illustrate this graphically, to correspond to Fig. 4.3. Find the distribution function and illustrate this graphically. Suggest a physical situation in which this distribution might be relevant.

5.3 For the distribution of Exercise 5.2, find the m.g.f. Hence find the m.g.f. of the sum of two independent observations from this distribution; and show that the probability distribution of the sum is not of the same form (with the same or different a).

5.4 In a factory, two machines produce the same type of electrical component. From machine 1, a sample of N_1 members is taken; each is tested, and r_1 of the N_1 are found to be defective. From machine 2, N_2 and r_2 are similarly found. The machines in fact produce proportions P_1, P_2 of defectives, respectively, and individual defectives occur independently so that the conditions of the binomial distribution obtain for each machine. Find the m.g.f. of (r_1+r_2). Show that the distribution of (r_1+r_2) is binomial if $P_1=P_2$, but not if $P_1 \neq P_2$.

5.5 The variates x, y, z, which are all necessarily $\geqslant 0$, have as their p.d.f.'s
$$f_1(x) = e^{-x},$$
$$f_2(y) = e^{-y},$$
$$f_3(z) = z e^{-z}.$$

Sketch the forms of these functions. By finding m.g.f.'s or otherwise, prove that the distribution of the sum of a value from the x distribution and an independent value from the y distribution is identical with the distribution of z.

5.6 Extend equation (5.36) to the term in θ^4, and by use of (A9) with $k=4$ prove that for the Poisson distribution

$$\mu_4 = \mu + 3\mu^2.$$

5.7 In Exercise 3.7, find the expectation and variance of the rateable value assigned to a house whose 'correct' value is £7000. Repeat on the assumption that the average of A and B is adopted.

5.8 The variates x, y can take any one of 5 pairs of values, with probabilities $f(x,y)$ as follows:

x	-1	0	1	2	3
y	-2	-1	0	1	2
$f(x,y)$	0·3	0·1	0·2	0·3	0·1

Find by direct calculation

(i) $E(x)$
(ii) $E(y)$
(iii) $Var(x)$—the variance of x
(iv) $Var(y)$
(v) $E[(x-y)]$
(vi) $Var[(x-y)]$
(vii) $E[(x+y)]$
(viii) $Var[(x+y)]$

5.9 Repeat Exercise 5.8 with

x	-1	0	1	2	3
y	-1	1	-2	2	0
$f(x,y)$	0·3	0·1	0·2	0·3	0·1

5.10 In Exercises 5.8 and 5.9, verify that

$$Var[(x+y)] + Var[(x-y)] = 2\,Var(x) + 2\,Var(y).$$

Illustrate this by constructing a third p.d.f. Prove that the result is completely general.

Chapter 6

MEANS

6.1 THE USE OF MEANS

The method of analysing the results of Experiment TWO already described (sections 3.1, 3.7, 4.2, 5.2) is logically valid but obviously crude. It classifies each pair of rats on the basis of which treatment is associated with the higher of the two rates of oxygen uptake, but pays no attention to the magnitudes of differences. If α and δ, the symbols denoting which treatment has the higher value, occur about equally often, the conclusion reached will be that evidence of any difference between treatments is negligible, even though the α records may show large differences in the observed rates of oxygen uptake and the δ records only small differences in the reverse direction.

The method will be very suitable if chief interest attaches to the frequency with which an animal on treatment A will show a greater rate of uptake than one on D. Often, however, the average value for the difference in rates, or the corresponding quantity for other variates in other experiments, is of major importance. To this, a fundamental theorem on means is relevant.

6.2 THE CENTRAL LIMIT THEOREM

This is one of the most remarkable theorems of statistics. In broad terms, it states that $\bar{x}$, the mean of n independent observations from a distribution of x with p.d.f. $f(x)$, has a probability distribution that is almost independent of the form of $f(x)$. The proof here is not completely rigorous or in the most general form possible, but it is correct in essential features and shows clearly the form of the argument.

If the m.g.f. of x exists, (5.27) states

$$M_{\bar{x}-\mu}(\theta) = \left[M_{x-\mu}\left(\frac{\theta}{n}\right) \right]^n. \qquad (6.1)$$

Now write

$$t = (\bar{x}-\mu)\sqrt{(n/\mu_2)}, \tag{6.2}$$

where n is the number of values of x from which $\bar{x}$ is calculated and μ_k is the central moment of x of order k. Then by (4.41)

$$M_t(\theta) = \left[M_{x-\mu}\left(\frac{\theta}{\sqrt{(n\mu_2)}}\right)\right]^n. \tag{6.3}$$

But, as in section 4.10 and (A10),

$$M_{x-\mu}(\theta) = 1+\mu_2\frac{\theta^2}{2!}+\mu_3\frac{\theta^3}{3!}+\dots. \tag{6.4}$$

Therefore, by expansion as a power series (A28–A31),

$$\log M_t(\theta) = \frac{\theta^2}{2}+\text{terms with factors } n^{-\frac{1}{2}}, n^{-1}, n^{-\frac{3}{2}}, \dots.$$

Existence of the m.g.f. of x implies that the μ_k are finite, and consequently

$$\log M_t(\theta) \to \frac{\theta^2}{2} \quad \text{as } n \to \infty. \tag{6.5}$$

Therefore

$$M_t(\theta) \to e^{\frac{1}{2}\theta^2} \quad \text{as } n \to \infty. \tag{6.6}$$

From section 5.8, and particularly equation (4.47), it follows that t has the Normal distribution $N(0, 1)$, often known as the *standardised* Normal distribution. This distribution has arisen without any assumptions about the form of $f(x)$ or its parameters, beyond the assumption that the m.g.f. exists.

Now from (4.40), (4.41), it is easily verified (A32–A35) that, if a variate y has the distribution $N(0, 1)$ and c, d are constants, the variate $(cy+d)$ has the distribution $N(d, c^2)$. Since from (6.2)

$$\bar{x} = t\sqrt{\left(\frac{\mu_2}{n}\right)}+\mu, \tag{6.7}$$

it follows that the distribution of $\bar{x}$ tends to the form $N(\mu, \mu_2/n)$ as n becomes large.

6.3   IMPORTANCE OF THE NORMAL DISTRIBUTION

Because the standard deviation (section 4.9) of a distribution is wanted so frequently, a symbol for it is useful, and σ is therefore not restricted to representing the S.D. of a Normal distribution. For any distribution that possesses a second moment,

$$\sigma^2 = \mu_2 \tag{6.8}$$

is customarily written. Moreover, though μ or μ_1' are general symbols for the mean of any distribution, ξ will now be written for the mean of a particular distribution of x.

Results in sections 5.8, 6.2 may now be expressed concisely as two theorems. Both refer to $\bar{x}$, the mean of n independent observations from a distribution of x with mean ξ, variance σ^2, for which

$$t = (\bar{x} - \xi)\sqrt{n}/\sigma \qquad (6.9)$$

is defined. These with Theorems III–VI of section 8.3 are vitally important to statistical analysis.

THEOREM I

If the distribution of x is $N(\xi, \sigma^2)$, then that of t is $N(0, 1)$ and that of $\bar{x}$ is $N(\xi, \sigma^2/n)$.

Equations (4.47), (5.46), (A32–A35) contain all that is necessary for proving this theorem.

THEOREM II

If the distribution of x is *not* Normal, that of t tends to $N(0, 1)$ as n becomes large. Moreover, the distribution of $\bar{x}$ and $N(\xi, \sigma^2/n)$ become asymptotically identical as n increases.

This is what has been proved in section 6.2.

Less capable of exact expression is the fact that the approach to Normality stated in the central limit theorem is very rapid if the distribution of x is even 'approximately' Normal. Statisticians have studied this in two ways. One is to investigate mathematically the form of the distribution of $\bar{x}$ from distributions of specific non-Normal types, and to examine measures of the departure from Normality for particular values of n. The other way is to select large numbers of independent sets of n values (say for $n = 5$, 10, 20, etc.) as numerical values from a distribution, and to investigate empirically the characteristics of the frequency distributions of their means.

In fact, the approach to Normality is much more rapid than many might suspect from the statements made so far. For example, suppose that x has what is for obvious reasons termed a *rectangular distribution*:

$$\left. \begin{aligned} f(x) &= \frac{1}{2a} \quad \text{for } -a \leqslant x \leqslant a \\ &= 0 \quad \text{otherwise.} \end{aligned} \right\} \qquad (6.10)$$

Then it is easily verified that

$$\xi = 0, \qquad (6.11)$$
$$\sigma^2 = a^2/3, \qquad (6.12)$$

and as n becomes large the distribution of $\bar{x}$ tends to the form $N(0, a^2/3n)$. The original distribution could scarcely be described as much like the Normal, but even with $n = 10$ the distribution of $\bar{x}$ is well approximated by the limiting form, and with $n = 20$ the approximation is very close. If $f(x)$ itself had been a little nearer to Normal form, still more rapid approach to Normality with increasing n would have been experienced.

Many measurements made in the course of scientific and technological investigations are in fact roughly Normal in the forms of their distributions. Among them are measurements as diverse as heights of individual men in a country, weights of wheat produced on different but equal areas of land, breaking strengths of individual metal bars of a particular type, percentages of solids in the milk of individual cows, and times required by individuals to complete a standard physical or mental test. None of these can be exactly Normally distributed: one good reason is that, however large ξ and however small σ may be, $N(\xi, \sigma^2)$ always allows the occurrence of negative values of x albeit with very small probability. Nevertheless, all of them are likely to be sufficiently close to Normality for means of even as few as five values to be safely assumed approximately Normal in distribution. Trouble seldom arises unless values of $\bar{x}$ very different from the mean of the population must be discussed; the Normal approximation is likely to be poor in the extreme 'tails' of the distribution.

*6.4   THE CAUCHY DISTRIBUTION

Lest belief in Normality should seem too easy, a mention of one well-known distribution that does not satisfy the conditions for the central limit theorem may be useful. The Cauchy distribution has the p.d.f.

$$f(x) = \frac{a}{b + (x - c)^2}, \tag{6.13}$$

where a, b, c are parameters. This is easily shown (A36, A37) to represent a p.d.f. provided that a, b are positive and

$$\pi a = \sqrt{b}. \tag{6.14}$$

However, no moments of the distribution exist: all the integrals required for these fail to converge! In particular, even the integral

$$\int_{-\infty}^{\infty} x f(x)\, dx$$

is very easily seen to have no finite value. Although the distribution is obviously symmetrical about $x = c$, this is not strictly the mean, and no quantity analogous to σ^2 can be obtained. Hence the conditions of the central limit theorem are not met, and there is no reason to expect an approach to Normality in the distribution of $\bar{x}$.

In fact, this distribution has a very remarkable property. Whatever the magnitude of n, the distribution of $\bar{x}$ is identical with that of x itself! This is readily proved for $n=2$, and a proof by induction can be given, but details are not presented here.

6.5   The Normal Distribution Function

Now that the importance of the role to be played by the Normal distribution is becoming clear, the need to use its distribution function will be realised. For $N(0, 1)$ the distribution function (the probability that a single value from the distribution is less than a specified T) is, by (5.14),

$$F(T) = \int_{-\infty}^{T} \frac{1}{\sqrt{(2\pi)}}\, e^{-\frac{1}{2}t^2}\, dt. \tag{6.15}$$

As stated in section 5.3, this cannot be evaluated in terms of known functions of T. Numerical integration is possible; extensive tables of the function exist, Table 5.2 being a short extract from these.

Suppose that circumstances provide data from which a statistic t_0 is calculated, where for the present $t_0 \geqslant 0$ is assumed, the calculations being according to equation (6.9) or some equivalent. Then it may be of interest to enquire into the probability that a single value of t from $N(0, 1)$ would equal or exceed t_0. Evidently (cf. (5.6))

$$Pr(t \geqslant t_0) = 1 - F(t_0). \tag{6.16}$$

Sometimes the interest may lie in considering whether the value of t independent of sign would exceed t_0; by symmetry

$$Pr(|t| \geqslant t_0) = Pr(t \geqslant t_0) + Pr(t \leqslant -t_0)$$
$$= 2[1 - F(t_0)]. \tag{6.17}$$

The function $Gp(t_0)$, symbolising the *Gaussian probability* associated with t_0, will be defined by

$$Gp(t_0) = Pr(t \geqslant t_0) \tag{6.18}$$

without restriction on the sign of t_0. This is not a standard notation, but is convenient here. Note that

$$Gp(t_0) = F(-t_0) = 1 - F(t_0). \tag{6.19}$$

For many purposes an inverse form of table is more useful than Table 5.2, this having $F(T)$, $Gp(T)$, or $2Gp(T)$ as argument and showing corresponding values of each. Table 6.1 is an extract from such a table of *Standard Normal Deviates*. Negative values of t_0 can be dealt with by symmetry; except that (6.17) is inapplicable, the same equations hold.

TABLE 6.1

Deviates of N(0, 1) for specified probabilities

$F(T)$	0·50	0·80	0·90	0·95	0·975	0·990	0·995	0·9995
$Gp(T)$	0·50	0·20	0·10	0·05	0·025	0·010	0·005	0·0005
$2Gp(T)$	1·00	0·40	0·20	0·10	0·050	0·020	0·010	0·0010
T	0·000	0·842	1·282	1·645	1·960	2·326	2·576	3·291

6.6   USE OF THE NORMAL DISTRIBUTION

The use of the Normal distribution can now be illustrated on results from Experiment TWO, and contrasted with the use of the binomial distribution. Suppose that the rate of oxygen uptake has been measured on a sample of cells from each of the 32 rats and the difference between treatments A and D has been calculated for each pair of litter mates. Write x for this difference (taken as $A–D$), supposed measured in units of 10^{-9} litres per mg dry weight per hour. Consider the 16 hypothetical values of x in Table 6.2.

TABLE 6.2

Differences between rats on treatments A, D in Experiment TWO
(hypothetical results)

(units of 10^{-9} litres per mg dry weight per hour)

16	12	15	9
14	−11	15	13
−4	6	−9	−4
3	13	−10	10

Suppose that these arise from a distribution with mean ξ, variance σ^2, and that the distribution is not violently unlike the Normal. By addition,

$$\Sigma x_i = 88, \tag{6.20}$$

$$\bar{x} = 88/16$$

$$= 5\cdot50. \tag{6.21}$$

From Theorem II, $\bar{x}$ has a distribution approximated by $N(\xi, \sigma^2/16)$. Hence

$$t_0 = \frac{5\cdot50 - \xi}{\sigma/4} \tag{6.22}$$

may be regarded as a statistic calculated from this experiment as one value from a distribution that is approximately $N(0, 1)$.

Further progress is impossible if nothing is known about σ. In sections 10.1, 10.2 will be discussed the standard procedure that involves replacement of σ by an estimate formed from the experimental results. The essentials of the logic can be illustrated here by supposing for the moment that a far less common situation obtains, namely that σ^2 is known. In particular, suppose that $\sigma^2 = 100$. Then (6.22) becomes

$$t_0 = \frac{5\cdot50 - \xi}{2\cdot50}. \tag{6.23}$$

To this quantity may be applied the same type of logic as in section 5.2, using a different consequence of the null hypothesis and a test of significance based upon the distribution of t. The null hypothesis stated in section 3.1, namely that treatments A and D do not differ in their effects on the rate of oxygen uptake by red cells, not only necessitates equation (3.1) but also

$$\xi = 0. \tag{6.24}$$

In (6.23), this gives

$$t_0 = 2\cdot2. \tag{6.25}$$

Exactly as in section 5.2, one may now ask about the probability that a value of t as great as or greater than t_0 would occur as a single value from the distribution $N(0, 1)$. To the extent that the central limit theorem provides an adequate approximation—and this will usually be very satisfactory with so large a value of n—equations (6.16), (6.18), and Table 6.1 provide the answer. From the Table

$$0\cdot025 > Gp(2\cdot2) > 0\cdot010, \tag{6.26}$$

and more exact tables give

$$Gp(2\cdot2) = 0\cdot014. \tag{6.27}$$

Therefore, if the null hypothesis is true, a value of $\bar{x}$ exceeding $\xi = 0$ by as much as or more than that found in the hypothetical experiment would occur with probability less than $0\cdot05$; on the assumption that $0\cdot05$ has again been chosen as the criterion for significance, the null hypothesis is now rejected and the conclusion drawn that in reality $\xi > 0$.

If the investigator is convinced that treatment A may *increase* the rate of oxygen uptake relative to treatment D but certainly will not *decrease* it, this is a reasonable argument to adopt. He may adduce evidence from other sources that $\xi < 0$ is wholly implausible. He is then interested only in testing whether $\xi = 0$ is seriously contradicted by the data from his experiment in a manner that indicates that in reality ξ exceeds zero. Of course, on account of the variability inherent in his animals, $\bar{x}$ might have happened to be negative, but a result such as $\bar{x} = -3 \cdot 5$ or even $\bar{x} = -16 \cdot 2$ he is prepared to regard merely as evidence against any difference and not as an indication that $\xi < 0$.

Although this may be entirely rational and self-consistent, such knowledge is perhaps rarer than some would expect. In other circumstances, the difference between a pair of treatments may be approached with a more open mind. The null hypothesis $\xi = 0$ may still be of interest, but the question asked may be whether a deviation as large as $\bar{x}$ *in either direction* is plausible on this hypothesis. The test of significance must be based on $|t|$ instead of t. Equation (6.17) becomes relevant in place of (6.16). With $t = 2 \cdot 2$ as before, evidently $2Gp(t)$ lies between $0 \cdot 05$ and $0 \cdot 02$, being more exactly about $0 \cdot 028$. In respect of the probability $0 \cdot 05$ as the criterion for significance, the verdict again is that $\bar{x}$ deviates significantly from zero and the null hypothesis is to be rejected.

Although the two significance tests have been described in terms of first calculating $Gp(t_0)$ or $2Gp(t_0)$ and then comparing with the $0 \cdot 05$ criterion, exactly the same conclusions will follow by comparing t_0 with $1 \cdot 645$ or $|t_0|$ with $1 \cdot 960$ respectively. The numerical value of t_0 need not be calculated when inspection of other numerical values makes obvious whether t_0 or $|t_0|$ exceeds the tabulated value. The result for the example follows because

$$|2 \cdot 2| > 1 \cdot 960; \tag{6.28}$$

the finding of $\bar{x} = -5 \cdot 5$ would have led to the same conclusion because

$$|-2 \cdot 2| > 1 \cdot 960. \tag{6.29}$$

Similarly, if a probability of $0 \cdot 01$ were to be made the criterion for significance the two types of test would involve comparison with $2 \cdot 326$ and $2 \cdot 576$ respectively (Table 6.1).

Of course, if $\xi > 0$ had been implausible, and only $\xi < 0$ relevant for consideration as an alternative to $\xi = 0$, the appropriate significance test at probability $0 \cdot 05$ would have been to see whether or not $t_0 < -1 \cdot 645$.

In this discussion, the value of the statistic t calculated from a particular experiment has been distinguished by a suffix. This distinction is unnecessary in ordinary statistical practice, but it may aid the understanding of the argument at this first presentation.

6.7 SINGLE AND DOUBLE TAILS

The tests based on t and $|t|$ are commonly referred to as single tailed and double tailed, or unilateral and bilateral, since they relate to deviations in one and in two 'tails' of the distribution curve respectively. For most purposes, the double-tailed approach is the more appropriate, and hereafter this is assumed unless the contrary is stated.

6.8 FIDUCIAL AND CONFIDENCE LIMITS

Other null hypotheses, specifying other values of ξ, may be tested by appropriate substitutions in (6.23). For example, suppose a null hypothesis were to be stated that rats on treatment A on average have rates of oxygen uptake exceeding those of rats on treatment D by $97 \cdot 5 \times 10^{-10}$ litres per mg per hour. This may be written

$$\xi = 9 \cdot 75. \tag{6.30}$$

By substitution in (6.23),

$$t_0 = \frac{5 \cdot 50 - 9 \cdot 75}{2 \cdot 50} = -1 \cdot 70. \tag{6.31}$$

The single-tailed probability of a deviation at least as extreme is

$$Pr(t < -1 \cdot 70) = Pr(t > 1 \cdot 70)$$
$$= Gp(1 \cdot 70)$$
$$< 0 \cdot 05, \tag{6.32}$$

by reference to Table 6.1. If the investigator is quite convinced that ξ cannot exceed 9·75 and has no interest in this possibility, a significance test at the level of 0·05 leads to the conclusion that the null hypothesis is untenable and therefore that ξ is less than 9·75. On the other hand, the double-tailed probability associated with the same t_0 is

$$2Gp(1 \cdot 70) > 0 \cdot 05. \tag{6.33}$$

Hence $\xi = 9 \cdot 75$ is not rejected as a plausible null hypothesis if the possibility of departures from it in either direction is under consideration.

Although occasionally a null hypothesis such as (6.30) may be interesting, only rarely does a specific alternative to (6.24) need to be tested. More important is a technique for deriving a range within which plausible values of ξ must lie. By equating $|t_0|$ to the double-tailed value of T in Table 6.1 for a stated probability, two limiting values of ξ may be found as the largest and smallest that are not rejected by a test based upon this probability. In the numerical example, any ξ satisfying

$$\left|\frac{5\cdot 50 - \xi}{2\cdot 50}\right| < 1\cdot 960 \qquad (6.34)$$

will not be rejected by a significance test at probability $0\cdot 05$. The limits are

$$\left.\begin{array}{l} \xi_U = 5\cdot 50 + 1\cdot 960 \times 2\cdot 50 = 10\cdot 40, \\ \xi_L = 5\cdot 50 - 1\cdot 960 \times 2\cdot 50 = 0\cdot 60. \end{array}\right\} \qquad (6.35)$$

More generally,

$$\left.\begin{array}{l} \xi_U = \bar{x} + T\sigma/\sqrt{n} \\ \xi_L = \bar{x} - T\sigma/\sqrt{n} \end{array}\right\}, \qquad (6.36)$$

where T is so chosen that $2Gp(T)$ equals the critical probability.

In the example, for a probability $0\cdot 01$ the limits are $11\cdot 94$ and $-0\cdot 94$; the occurrence of opposite sign corresponds with the fact that $\bar{x}$ is not significantly different from zero at this probability level.

These limits are known as upper and lower *fiducial* or *confidence limits* to ξ, at the probability

$$1 - 2Gp(T);$$

it is customary to speak of limits at a probability $0\cdot 95$, rather than $0\cdot 05$, for the convenience of subsequent terminology. In a special sense, there may be said to be a *fiducial probability* of $0\cdot 95$ that ξ for the experiment lies between $0\cdot 60$ and $10\cdot 40$. Alternatively, the investigator may regard himself as having a degree of confidence measured by the value $0\cdot 95$ that ξ lies between $0\cdot 60$ and $10\cdot 40$; if he habitually makes calculations of this kind, and each time concludes with a statement 'ξ lies between ξ_U and ξ_L', 95 per cent of his statements will be true.

There are important logical distinctions between fiducial and confidence limits, but here as in many simple problems they are numerically identical. The subject cannot now be discussed. In scientific research, where the best possible use is to be made of a single experiment as a foundation for general inference, the fiducial outlook is often the more appropriate. In the testing of factory products, where routine 'experiments' may be intended merely as confirmation that successive batches of articles do not fall below an agreed standard, the notion of confidence statements may be preferred.

Occasionally single-tailed limits are wanted instead of the double-tailed described here.

6.9 MEMORY

The practising statistician finds it convenient to remember some rough approximations corresponding to Table 6.1. The most useful are shown in Table 6.3.

TABLE 6.3

Easily remembered standard normal deviates

$2Gp(T)$	1/2	1/3	1/20	1/100	1/1000
T	2/3	1·0	2·0	2·5	3·3

Familiarity with these enables rapid assessments and judgements to be made and encourages a sensible appreciation of numerical records. This may be compared to the foreign traveller's use of easily remembered exchange rates: £1 is not the exact equal of $2½, nor is 1 Swiss franc exactly 2/–, but the British visitor to New York or Zürich will find these approximations convenient.

*6.10 NORMAL TEST ON BINOMIAL DATA

The test of significance in section 5.2 is laborious to compute when N is large. Fortunately this is just the situation that permits the central limit theorem to provide an approximation, with the aid of the variance found in section 4.6. An example should suffice to illustrate the procedure.

A cubical die of standard pattern is thrown 900 times and shows the face 6 in 177 of these trials. Are there clear indications of bias? Here the null hypothesis is that $P = 1/6$ in a binomial distribution; by (4.15)

$$E(r) = 900/6 = 150, \qquad (6.37)$$

and by (4.24)

$$Var(r) = 900 \times \tfrac{1}{6} \times \tfrac{5}{6} = 125. \qquad (6.38)$$

The observation $r = 177$ leads to

$$t_0 = \frac{177 - 150}{\sqrt{125}}$$

$$= 2\cdot41. \qquad (6.39)$$

This may be referred to Table 6.1. If the interest lies solely in the possibility that the proportion of sixes is excessively high (as might be the case if dishonesty in a game were suspected), a single-tailed test will be chosen; if deviations from the hypothetical P in either direction are of equal interest (as might be relevant to a purely scientific interest in the perfect balance of the cube), a double-tailed test would be preferred. If the 0·05 significance level is being used, t_0 in (6.39) indicates a significant deviation from expectation with either test: in the face of this evidence, belief that this was a fair die fairly thrown may reasonably be rejected.

Such a test is a trustworthy approximation only when N is large and P not close to 0 or 1. A cautious rule would be not to rely on its results when either NP or $N(1-P)$ is less than 50 unless the indications on significance are very clear.

*6.11   A Very General Theorem

Suppose that an entirely general distribution of x has variance σ^2. Without loss of any essential generality, x may be supposed measured from the mean of the distribution. For any positive a, write $Q(a)$ for the probability that a single observation taken from the distribution lies outside the interval $(-a, a)$; that is to say, writing $f(x)$ as the p.d.f.,

$$Q(a) = \int_{-\infty}^{-a} f(x)\,dx + \int_{a}^{\infty} f(x)\,dx. \tag{6.40}$$

Note that if x had the distribution $N(0, \sigma^2)$ the function $Q(a)$ would be identical with $2Gp(a/\sigma)$, but here the discussion is intended to include distributions very far removed from Normality. Consider now three inequalities. The first is

$$\int_{-\infty}^{-a} x^2 f(x)\,dx \geqslant \int_{-\infty}^{-a} a^2 f(x)\,dx$$

$$= a^2 \int_{-\infty}^{-a} f(x)\,dx, \tag{6.41}$$

the truth of which is obvious, since the original integrand is non-negative throughout its range and has been replaced by an integrand less or equal to it for every x in the range. Similarly

$$\int_{a}^{\infty} x^2 f(x)\,dx \geqslant a^2 \int_{a}^{\infty} f(x)\,dx. \tag{6.42}$$

The p.d.f. is not necessarily symmetrical, and therefore corresponding integrals in (6.41), (6.42) need not be equal. Thirdly and very obviously

$$\int_{-a}^{a} x^2 f(x)\,dx \geqslant 0, \tag{6.43}$$

because the integrand is non-negative throughout its range. The integrals on the left of (6.41), (6.42), (6.43) sum to σ^2. Therefore

$$\sigma^2 \geqslant a^2 Q(a), \qquad (6.44)$$

whence for any value of a

$$Q(a) \leqslant \sigma^2/a^2. \qquad (6.45)$$

Replacement of integrals by sums gives a parallel proof for discrete distributions.

This remarkable result is known as the *Bienaymé–Tchebycheff inequality*. It is of great theoretical interest, but of limited practical importance because in most circumstances the inequality is so extreme. The three essential steps in the proof use '$\geqslant$' relations which can approach equality only for rather extraordinary distributions, so that for distributions such as are commonly encountered $Q(a)$ will be very much less than σ^2/a^2. For example, exact values for the distribution $N(0, 1)$ can be obtained from Table 5.2 as $[2 - 2F(a)]$ for any positive a, and compared with the statements from the inequality; Table 6.4 shows some comparisons.

TABLE 6.4

Comparison of exact probability and Bienaymé–Tchebycheff upper limit for the distribution $N(0, 1)$

a	Exact $Q(a)$ from Table 5.2	Upper limit to $Q(a)$ from (6.45)
1·0	0·318	1·00
1·5	0·134	0·44
2·0	0·046	0·25
2·5	0·0124	0·16
3·0	0·0026	0·11

Evidently if enough is known of a distribution to permit a statement that a probability is 0·012, the cruder statement that the probability is not greater than 0·16 is not very satisfying!

EXERCISES

6.1 A certain machine is required to operate continuously for a long period, except that brief interruptions can be tolerated when 'component A' fails; a new A must be inserted without delay. Supplies of

A are drawn from a source in which the 'life' is Normally distributed, with mean 1100 hours and standard deviation 190 hours. At the beginning of a leap year, a new *A* has been inserted. What is the probability that by the end of the year not more than 8 replacements have been needed. [Use Theorem I and equation (6.16).]

6.2 An industrial chemist has learned by experience that independent determinations of the percentage of constituent *B* present in a batch of raw material are approximately Normally distributed with standard deviation 0·6 per cent. How many determinations must he make on one batch in order that the probability of his mean differing from ξ by more than 0·2 per cent shall be at most 0·05 ? How many if this margin is reduced from 0·2 per cent to 0·1 per cent ? How many, under each condition, if the probability is to be at most 0·01 ?

6.3 Find explicit algebraic expressions for the distribution functions of *x*, *y*, *z*, three variates all > 0 for which the p.d.f.'s are

$$f_1(x) = \alpha e^{-\alpha x},$$

$$f_2(y) = \beta^2 y e^{-\beta y},$$

$$f_3(z) = \tfrac{1}{2}\gamma^3 z^2 e^{-\gamma z}.$$

With the aid of appropriate tables, sketch the forms of the three distribution functions for the cases $\alpha = 1$, $\beta = 2$, $\gamma = 3$, using the same scales for all the sketches.

6.4 By use of the integral

$$\int_{-\infty}^{\infty} \frac{du}{(1+u^2)\,[1+(z-u)^2]} = \frac{2\pi}{4+z^2}$$

or otherwise, prove that the mean of two observations from the distribution with p.d.f.

$$f(y) = \frac{1}{\pi(1+y^2)}$$

also has $f(y)$ as its p.d.f. [cf. section 6.4].

6.5 A coin is suspected to be biased in favour of heads, so as to have $P = 0·51$ for heads instead of $P = 0·50$. Discuss how to decide the number of spins of the coin needed in order to show a statistically significant deviation from the null hypothesis of perfect balance.

6.6 Sketch the p.d.f.

$$f(x) = -x/c \quad \text{for } -c \leqslant x \leqslant 0 \atop \left. \begin{array}{ll} = x/c & \text{for } 0 \leqslant x \leqslant c \\ = 0 & \text{otherwise.} \end{array} \right\}$$

Find the mean and variance and the distribution function, and sketch the distribution function. Discuss the form of the distribution of $\bar{x}\sqrt{n}$, where $\bar{x}$ is the mean of a sample of n and n is large.

6.7 Repeat the calculations in section 6.6, but suppose that the experiment included only 8 pairs of rats, the results being the first two columns of Table 6.2.

6.8 What differences will be made in the calculations of section 6.6 if the records in Table 6.2 are expressed in units of 10^{-8} litres per mg dry weight per hour? What changes, if any, are made in the conclusions?

6.9 Use equation (A33) to prove that if

$$z = cy + d$$

and y has any distribution for which the m.g.f. exists, then

$$\text{Mean of } z = c\mu + d$$
$$\text{Variance of } z = c^2 \mu_2,$$

where μ, μ_2 refer to y. The result is readily obtained by expressing the two factors on the right-hand side of (A33) as power series, multiplying term by term, and equating coefficients of θ, θ^2 with those on the left-hand aside.

6.10 The Poisson distribution (section 5.7) is useful for representing the occurrence of unrelated events in time, such as the frequency of calls entering a telephone switchboard, of faults in machinery, or of errors in typesetting. Experience has shown that a certain newspaper averages five compositor's errors per page, the distribution over individual pages being Poisson. After a reorganisation, the first issue of the newspaper is found to have 85 errors in its 20 pages. Discuss the evidence that the frequency of errors has been reduced. Three days later, a count of four issues shows a total of 356 errors in 80 pages. Discuss the evidence at this stage. Explain non-mathematically why an average of 4·25 errors per page may be judged a non-significant improvement yet an average of 4·45 errors per page is significantly less than 5 (significance level 0·05).

[Equations (5.36), (5.38) enables a method analogous to that of section 6.10 to be used.]

Chapter 7

RANDOMNESS AND RANDOMISING

7.1 SELECTION FROM A DISTRIBUTION

Nothing has yet been said about the mechanism of getting observations from a distribution. In one sense, this is inherent in the specification of a probability distribution. A statement that in a large bag of seeds of red and white poppies the probability distribution of the character 'white flower' is binomial with $P=0.2$ implies that successive seeds drawn from the bag *by a fair process* will behave in accordance with this distribution. Similarly, a statement (cf. Exercise 6.1) that the lengths of life for a particular type of automatic switch are distributed normally with mean 1100 hours, S.D. 190 hours implies that measurements of life on switches taken in a routine manner from stock will conform to $N(1100, 190^2)$.

In practice, unfortunately, differences may easily arise between the natural distribution of a character or a measurement in what might be termed a 'resting phase' and the effective distribution when records are made. The example of the poppy seeds can illustrate some of the possibilities: it does not suffice that the bag contains a large number of seeds one-fifth of which will produce white poppies. Consider the following:

(i) The seeds may not be thoroughly mixed in the bag. One extreme would be that of all the white poppy seeds being on top, so that the first few thousand seeds taken would almost certainly give white flowers! Alternatively, there may be local concentrations such as will arise if different seeds from one plant are likely to be 'clumped', a tendency for several hundred red seeds to occur together alongside a concentration of several hundred white. Of course there would be some mixing, but the drawing of seeds from one part of the bag might give a long sequence of one colour followed by a sequence of the other.

(ii) Possibility (i) does not depend upon any difference in appearance between the two types of seed. Alternatively, even though the seeds are well mixed in the bag, there may be characteristics (visual, tactile, or purely mechanical) that favour selection of one type. If the person responsible for taking seeds from the bag looks into the bag, he may be influenced by any colour differences in the seed-coat; white poppies may have a slightly different colour of seed and may be selected more often than once in five. If selection is entirely by touch, a difference in roughness or shape of seed could have a similar consequence, though perhaps this is scarcely likely with seeds as small as those of the poppy. Even if selection is achieved by allowing seeds to flow down a narrow channel, mechanical properties may encourage those of white poppies to move more rapidly than those of red, and so at first to be present in excess.

(iii) The colour of flower can be discovered only by growing a plant that bears at least one flower. The colour may be genetically determined; unless conditions for growth are very favourable, however, germination failures and damage by diseases and pests may affect the two types of seed differentially, so distorting the natural proportion of white poppies.

(iv) In this example, the observational and recording programme is unlikely to encounter difficulties, but in other quite similar circumstances these also may contribute to a discrepancy between the natural and the apparent or effective distribution. One possibility is that the flowering seasons for the two colours differ slightly, so that an enforced ending of observations on a particular day leaves a different proportion of white flowers among those already recorded from that which would be found among those classed as not yet flowered. A second possibility, if the two colours under study were less distinct than red and white, is that the observer errs occasionally in his classification.

Analogous possibilities could be presented in respect of the automatic switches. The stated definition may relate to the whole production of a factory, but switches made by one group of workers or one machine are likely to be packed together and these may not have the same distribution among themselves. A sequence of switches used is likely to come from one such batch until it is exhausted, and therefore may not be representative of the whole distribution.

These troubles are frequently termed sources of bias in the study of the natural distribution. The bias leads to the properties of the sample of individuals studied not corresponding satisfactorily with those of that population; the expectation of a statistic calculated from measurements made on the sample may not be in reality what theory would indicate for a sample of this size from the distribution. The alternative suggested here, discussion in terms of the original natural distribution and of the effective distribution that is observable, is in some respects more helpful. Avoidance of bias is equivalent to the taking of steps to ensure that the two distributions are identical (cf. section 12.4, where bias is given a more precise definition).

7.2 THE DANGERS OF BIAS

Once sources of bias have been recognised, it may be possible to devise special measures for their avoidance, though often this is far from easy. Greater danger lies in the unrecognised or ill-defined sources, and in unthinking assumptions that the distribution from which measurements are obtained is the same as the one intended for study. The only safe outlook is to regard the occurrence of biases as the usual state of affairs, avoidable only by positive action. In case of dispute whether or not a proposed procedure for selecting individuals from a population is biased, the onus should always lie with him who believes the procedure unbiased to prove his case rather than with his opponent to demonstrate a specific source of bias. Nevertheless, the experienced statistician will often be able to suggest where the chief dangers of bias lie even when he is faced with an entirely new problem.

'Of course the political opinions of women in a supermarket at noon will be representative of women in the general population.' But may not those who, for reasons of employment or health, habitually shop at a different time of day or depend entirely on telephone orders show some average difference in political outlook?

'Of course deaths among swallows ringed by an ornithologist will enable the natural death rate to be measured.' But may not the presence of a ring on the leg itself influence the hazards of a bird's life?

'Of course the relative frequencies of different blood groups in the population can be estimated from the records of donors held by transfusion services.' But is it certain that willingness to volunteer as a donor is wholly independent of blood group?

'Of course, a careful testing of every twentieth refrigerator from an assembly line will suffice for determination of the frequencies of various manufacturing faults.' But what happens if the workers responsible for the assembly learn to know when the twentieth is in their hands?

'Of course the sizes of potato tubers in a growing crop can be studied by digging 30 plants from the whole field and examining the tubers on these.' But if the person doing the digging has no objective rule, may he not be subconsciously influenced in his choice of 30 plants by luxuriance of leaf growth, whether or not a plant is flowering, discoloration of leaves by disease, and other factors that could easily be associated with tuber development? If he has an objective rule, how is this to be phrased?

'Of course a study of family background of children in a large school can be kept of manageable size by including only every tenth name in the school register?' But, if the register is alphabetic on surnames, this is likely to ensure that the sample does not include any pairs of brothers or sisters; will this be relevant to the matters studied?

'Of course a survey of sickness and ill-health could be based on every twentieth house or flat in a neighbourhood.' But if the area has been fairly uniformly planned this could introduce a predominance of more northerly members of semi-detached pairs, of flats on the east side of blocks rather than the west, or even of corner houses which are often somewhat larger; may not these be associated with family size, economic circumstances, occupation, and other matters that are in turn related to health?

'Of course the quality of nylon stockings produced in a factory can be adequately supervised by breaking open and inspecting two cartons of 50 pairs daily.' But one carton is likely to contain stockings from a single machine among the many in the factory; variability within a carton may be much less than the total variability over the output of the factory for a day, and the inspection records may show relatively large oscillations from day to day because the stockings come from two different machines each day. In the light of these considerations, will the proposed samples enable the management adequately to maintain a high uniform quality for all its production?

All the questions above invite the answer that the proposed method of selection is unsatisfactory. This is not necessarily so, for in some circumstances the methods may be adequate. The common feature is that each proposal aims at substituting a readily observable section of the population for the whole, and omitting parts of the population that are less accessible. The notion of taking a *sample*—30 plants from 50 000 in a field, 5 per cent of refrigerators, or a small proportion of the swallows in a region—is legitimate and valuable, but the methods proposed above or the types of inference to be based on the results may introduce biases on account of implicit assumptions. These assumptions cannot be put to the test except by conducting a study in two distinct ways and comparing the results. Moreover, failure to find any difference between the natural and the effective distribution on one occasion is no guarantee that the same will be true for closely related material on a later occasion. The wise investigator always fears that any feature of a population that makes certain of its members more accessible for study may be associated with the variates whose study is to be undertaken.

7.3 PURPOSIVE AND HAPHAZARD SELECTION

Even when no difficulties of accessibility arise, the mechanics of taking a fair sample presents problems. One may wish to choose for further study 100 households in a town, 100 trees in one square mile of forest, or 100 transistors from the total output of one kind by a factory in a week. *Purposive selection*, in which an investigator tries to judge by inspection which individuals to take as representative of the population, has all the dangers of uncontrolled subjective choice. For example, the selection of 100 trees from the forest might tend towards trees somewhat larger than average and is even more likely to give a predominance of trees of moderate size with under-representation of the very large and the very small. However honest his intentions, an investigator who attempts such selection is almost certain to distort the distribution in some manner, and different investigators will exercise subjective judgement in different ways. An alternative sometimes tried may be termed *haphazard selection*: the investigator now endeavours to choose members from the population without any recognised aim. He may wander casually in the forest marking trees for taking, or put dots on a map and find the nearest households, or pick transistors in a haphazard manner from a production line or a store. But again subjective influences are likely to operate in an ill-defined and undesirable manner.

7.4 RANDOM SELECTION

The only safe way of overcoming these difficulties is to establish a (1, 1) correspondence between the population and a truly random sequence of numbers, and then to use these random numbers as the basis of selection. By a random sequence is meant a sequence such as might emerge as successive drawings in a fair lottery. If 100 individuals are to be selected from a population of 5000, one can regard the population as numbered from 0001 to 5000; the first 100 numbers in a lottery sequence such as 0163, 4397, 1612, 0092, ..., then identify those to be selected.

The logical difficulty of defining a fair lottery remains and will not be discussed here. Essentially it is that 'fairness' is definable only in terms of equally probable alternatives, and one cannot find a point of entry to the circuit 'probability' 'randomness', 'fairness', 'probability'. For the immediate purpose, an intuitive understanding based upon a purely mechanical device will suffice. A die might be cut from uniform material in the shape of a regular icosahedron; two of the 20 faces could then be marked with each of the digits 0, 1, ..., 9. Throwing or rolling the die generates a sequence of digits which will approach the ideal of randomness to the extent that the die approaches perfect uniformity and regularity, provided that the thrower has no knowledge of the orientation with which he starts and therefore cannot exercise conscious or unconscious control. The Japanese Standards Association in fact markets such dice as aids to the practice of random selection.

Instead of conducting a lottery or using special dice, recourse may be had to various published *tables of random numbers*. These are merely printed lists of the sequences of digits obtained by some of the many possible devices. A list of thousands of digits may be printed, perhaps arranged in groups of 4 or 5 for ease of reading; for example

01634 43979 84138 16120 93955
50014 00926 22189 ...

A sample from 5000 could be drawn by the following rule: Of each group of five digits, neglect the last one; read the first four; if these are in the range 0001 to 5000, interpret as one for the sample; otherwise, ignore and continue with the next group of five; if a number once selected occurs again, ignore the second appearance; continue until 100 different individuals have been obtained. This rule will produce the sample numbers listed in the preceding paragraph.

It is not the present purpose to discuss all ways in which such random numbers can be used to give an entirely objective and representative selection. If trees in a forest are regularly spaced, they can obviously be numbered either consecutively 1, 2, 3, ..., or on a two-co-ordinate system and the method applied. Similarly households in a town might be numbered consecutively with the aid of a street directory or an electoral roll. Selection of the transistors might be more complicated. Various tricks and dodges for doing this kind of thing expeditiously are part of the stock-in-trade of the applied statistician. Here all that need be emphasised is that existence of a table of random numbers constitutes the basic equipment.

Nor will details of the construction of random numbers be described here. A finely constructed roulette wheel with 10 equal sectors is one possibility; a more sophisticated version might have a rotating pointer illuminated and read at instants controlled by the emission of particles from a radioactive source. An entirely different method is to take digits from standard tables of mathematical functions. This obviously requires care, for the behaviour of, say, the fourth digit in successive entries in a table of log Z depends very much on the tabulation interval for Z. A table containing as many as a million random digits has been published as an aid to statistical practice. More recently, for use with high-speed computers, techniques for generating *pseudo-random numbers* have been devised. These techniques produce determinate sequences of numbers which appear to possess features of true random sequences adequate for practical purposes. One such technique is:

Evaluate, for $i = 1, 2, 3, \ldots,$

$$S_i = 5^{17} S_{i-1} \pmod{2^{40}}, \tag{7.1}$$

beginning with

$$S_0 = 1.$$

Then write

$$m_i = S_i/2^{40}. \tag{7.2}$$

The successive m_i can be regarded as random values in the interval $(0, 1)$. In particular, the first digits of the m_i may be used as a random sequence of the digits $0, 1, 2, \ldots, 9$.

An electronic computer can produce such series of numbers at great speed, and can use them in theoretical studies.

7.5 PROBABILITY DISTRIBUTIONS ONCE MORE

In all earlier development of the theory of distributions and derivation of their properties, reference has been made to values of variates in these distributions. Implicit in this is always the assumption that the values are randomly selected from their distributions. For example, the properties of means discussed in section 5.5 are true only in so far as the observations from which the means are calculated have been selected at random from their distributions. In a sense such statements are tautological. The requirement is simply that the effective distribution—the distribution of the observations used—shall be identical with the original or natural distribution.

Practical procedures for achieving random selection in the taking of observations from the distribution of a continuous variate need not be discussed here; evidently questions of a limiting process and adequate approximation thereto arise, though the ideas are intuitively obvious.

The point to be emphasised is that a statement such as 'x_1 is an observation from a distribution for which the p.d.f. is $f(x)$' must always be interpreted as implying random selection: one must not sample in such a way as to favour positive values of x at the expense of negative, or rational values at the expense of irrational, except in so far as the form of $f(x)$ affects the relative chances of selection. Also excluded, of course, are dishonesties such as continuing to sample at random until an observation is obtained that is positive, or for which the first digit is even, and then using this as x_1! Any such procedure produces a modified effective distribution.

These notions may seem to be receiving unnecessary stress, but failure to take full account of them is a fertile source of misleading statistical practice and mistaken statistical theory.

*7.6   SAMPLING, SAMPLE SURVEY, AND UNCONTROLLED OBSERVATION

Statistical theory has many important applications in connection with inference from samples. This book has been written around planned experimentation rather than sampling, because a wider range of theory and method can thereby be introduced, but sampling must receive a mention.

In the present chapter, indeed, the emphasis so far has been on problems of sampling. A milk depot needs to estimate the percentage fat in milk from each producer, by regular analysis on small volumes. A manufacturer of electronic equipment, or of rubber tyres, needs to estimate the durability of his products by testing small numbers to the point of collapse or destruction. An entomologist estimates the number of insects of a certain species present in an area by actually counting on perhaps 0·01 per cent of the area.

In these and many other instances, sampling is inescapable, either because to measure the whole universe involved would defeat its own ends by destroying a wanted commodity (the milk or the tyres) or because of limitations on the time and labour available. Not only is the statistician needed as an advisor on selecting the sample, along the lines indicated earlier in this chapter, but also he can help in deciding the size of the sample and in drawing probabilistic inferences from the results by using techniques that parallel those described in other chapters; for example, he might make statements about the average mileage that tyres will survive, or the proportion that will be good for more than a specified mileage.

Sample survey is the name applied when these ideas are extended to the study of questionnaires addressed to units of a population, in place of single questions or measurements. A sample of milk producers may be questioned on many aspects of the feeding, management, and productivity of their herds. A sample of motorists may be questioned about the tyres they use and associated factors such as type of car, pattern of use, and driving skill. In execution, a survey will be much more complex than is sampling for a single character, but the same statistical problems arise.

Planned sampling and sample surveys always require consideration of alternative methods of sample selection. Often many forms of random selection are possible, differing not only in trivial detail of how random numbers are prepared but also in more important respects related to classifications within the population. Any proposals for non-random selection usually require discussion against a background of the ideal random plan.

One other type of information from which it is desired to draw inferences about the quantitative properties of distributions may be described as *uncontrolled observation*. Measurements on skeletons unearthed by an archaeologist tell something about the physique of a long-extinct community. Counts of growth rings on trees chosen for felling in a forest tell something about the age distribution in the forest. Analyses of meteorites help to inform us on extra-terrestrial chemistry. In these and other instances, the investigator has no control over selection of the sample, and even to specify the population sampled may be difficult, but some tentative quantitative assessments may be possible. The class of problem is mentioned here only for contrast with what has gone before; the statistician may still play an important role but his duties are less well defined.

The planning of sampling and of sample surveys benefits enormously from full utilisation of whatever information on the population (or on similar populations) is already available. The optimal strategy for sampling depends greatly on accessibility of the units of the population, on time and labour available, on costs of various operations, and on the intended use of the results. Hence a plan recommended for routine sampling of milk might be very different from one for routine sampling of petroleum, a survey of children's health in Mexico would differ in many respects from the plan recommended in Belgium, and a scheme of sampling inspection proved excellent for controlling the quality of nylon stockings might be little help in designing a scheme suitable for a factory engaged in canning vegetables. The frequent appeal to special conditions makes this branch of applied statistics less suitable as a background for a textbook on statistical theory.

7.7 RANDOMISATION OF EXPERIMENTS

Despite the emphasis given above to selection of individuals from a population with a view to estimation of properties of the distribution, the concept of randomness and random selection is equally important in planned experimentation. The outlook of the investigator and of the statistician requires only slight modification.

Consider Experiment THREE. The 32 rats available must be divided between treatments A and D. The investigator may decide on general grounds how many he will allot to A and how many to D; commonly his decision will be to have 16 for each (section 8.6), and this will be assumed here though the essentials of the argument are the same if he chooses to have, say, 19 and 13. How is he to determine which particular animals are to be the 16 for A? To take the first 16 that emerge from a door in the cage may secure predominance of the most active; to take the first 16 caught by an assistant who puts his hand in the cage may bias selection towards the least active. Other possibilities may favour particular coat colours or particular parents. Of course there may be no reason to suppose that any of these characteristics of young rats is associated with the rate of oxygen uptake by red cells, but the investigator cannot afford to risk the possibility of an association that could ruin his experiment. To demonstrate that any association is neglible would require a more extensive research programme than Experiment THREE itself!

Randomisation provides the escape. The division of the 32 rats into 16 and 16 should be made completely at random, and this can be accomplished by allocating to A 16 selected at random from the 32, the remainder going to B. An objective system of numbering the rats must first be agreed; they may already be identified by numbers, or the numbering can be based on the order in which they emerge or are taken from the cage. Consideration of bias does not enter here, as long as whoever assigns the numbers does so in ignorance of the outcome of the next step. The only necessity is that the rats are hereafter identifiable by the numbers 1, 2, 3, ..., 32.

Next a (1, 1) correspondence is established between these numbers and a random sequence. There are many ways in which this can be done. For example, read a table of random numbers in pairs of digits; the numbers used illustratively in section 7.4 become:

01   63   44   39   79   84   13   81   61   20   ...

Ignore all numbers except those from 01 to 32. Allocate to A the rats identified by the first sixteen different numbers in this range, that is to say 01, 13, 20, ... This is time-consuming because 68 of the possible pairs of digits are useless. With a little extra effort, the pairs of digits 00 to 99 can be made to include the required range twice, so reducing the amount of scanning of the random number table. In reading, any digit-pair that is 50 or greater should have 50 subtracted from it, so that the sequence now is

$$01 \quad 13 \quad 44 \quad 39 \quad 29 \quad 34 \quad 13 \quad 31 \quad 11 \quad 20 \quad ...;$$

the rats numbered 01, 13, 29 (13 already taken), 31, 11, 20, ... are to be taken for A. The first method and its modification, as well as other alternatives that could be suggested, have the property that each of the $32!/(16!)^2$ possible ways of selecting 16 animals out of 32 has the same chance of being selected.

Experiment TWO is much simpler. Once it is agreed, as in section 3.1, that one rat from each of the 16 pairs is to be allotted to A, only 2^{16} arrangements are possible, about one-thousandth of the number for Experiment THREE. One can be obtained for use by selecting one number of each pair at random and allocating it to treatment A. For each pair, one digit in the table of random numbers suffices. The two rats are arbitrarily designated as '1' and '2'; if the digit is odd the rat 1 goes to A, if even (0 is even) rat 2 goes to A. Using the previous extract from a random number table (section 7.4), nine successive litters would contribute to A the rats numbered

$$2, 1, 2, 1, 2, 2, 1, 1, 1, ...$$

The difference between Experiments TWO and THREE in their randomisations is reflected in the appropriate methods of statistical analysis, as will become apparent. The randomisation of Experiment ONE will be mentioned later (sections 11.6, 11.8).

7.8   THE MERITS OF RANDOMISATION

The mechanical processes of randomisation are scarcely of great interest to the student of statistical theory. The principle is vitally important to the planning and conduct of research. *Indeed, it is scarcely too much to claim that the concept of randomising the allocation of experimental units to treatments is a contribution to the logic of interpreting experiments at least as important as the mathematical theory of statistical analysis.*

Only when a proper randomisation has been performed is the argument by significance tests and fiducial or confidence limits valid. Randomisation does not eliminate the inherent differences between the animals or guarantee that these are perfectly balanced over the two or more treatments. It recognises the inevitability of these differences and ensures that they are as likely to favour one treatment as another. They then contribute in proper proportions to the assessment of variance, or of any other measure of chance variation. Any significance test involves reference to a probability that a difference as large as that observed in the experiment would occur by chance; that chance includes exactly the possibility that an observed difference is due to the randomisation instead of to real effects of treatments. The full force of this will become clear only with increasing sophistication in statistical logic, but even the relative newcomer to the subject should be able to follow the argument in respect of a situation as simple as that of Experiment TWO.

No experiment using inherently variable subjects can entirely eliminate the possibility that a difference apparently due to differences of treatment is in reality a consequence of one treatment having had proportionately more brown-spotted rats than another (or more with low blood-calcium or more born on a Tuesday). Randomisation ensures that the risk of misleading conclusions from such causes can be made as small as is desired by sufficiently enlarging the experiment. On the other hand, a haphazard, purposive, or other subjective technique for allocating rats to treatments may permit a bias associated with coat-colour to continue however large the experiment, and 320 rats will be no more safeguard against false conclusions than 32.

In all previous and subsequent accounts of experiments, randomisation will be assumed. For example, the logic of section 6.6 is valid only if allocations to A, D were made by the method described at the end of section 7.7 or an equivalent method.

EXERCISES

7.1 Suggest a method for selecting 100 at random out of 5000 similar to that described at the beginning of section 7.4, but avoiding the 'wastage' of entries in the table of random numbers when the first digit in a group of five is 5, 6, 7, 8 or 9.

7.2 In the random selection described at the beginning of section 7.4, why would it be wrong to use 'overlapping' numbers, taking for the sample the individuals numbered 0163, 1634, 6344, 3443, 4439, 4397, 3979, . . . ?

7.3 Re-read section 7.7. Suggest a randomisation procedure for Experiment THREE for which only four of the possible digit-pairs are not usable in the allocation of rats to treatments.

4

7.4 In Experiment TWO, what criticisms could be made of a procedure
that allocates an animal from the first litter exactly as described in
section 7.7, but for subsequent litters merely alternates? That is to
say, if it begins with 2 as described, the allocation of first rats from
successive litters would be:

$$2, 1, 2, 1, 2, 1, 2, 1, 2, \ldots.$$

Chapter 8

DIFFERENCES BETWEEN MEANS

8.1 Experiment Three

Experiment THREE, as described in section 2.5, leaves open little choice for its design. Of the 32 animals, some must be allotted to A and some to D, and the only question remaining is that of how many should be placed in each category. In general, if a total of n animals is available, to use all will obviously be wise and they may be divided into n_1 for A, n_2 for D, where

$$n_1 + n_2 = n. \tag{8.1}$$

After the discussions in Chapter 7, the need to choose the n_1 rats out of n at random need not be emphasised. A method of doing this has been described in section 7.7; it ensures that every one of the $n!/n_1!n_2!$ possible allocations has the same probability of being chosen. The optimal value of n_1 to use (out of the possibilities $1, 2, 3, \ldots, n-1$) is considered in section 8.6.

For the present, suppose that a particular n_1 has been adopted and the experiment completed. The rate of oxygen uptake has been measured for red cells from each of the n rats. What form of statistical analysis is to be made and what kind of conclusions can be drawn? There is now no arrangement in pairs, and indeed n_1, n_2 may be unequal.

8.2 Distribution-free Methods

Section 5.2 presented a method of analysis for results from Experiment TWO that avoided assumptions about the probability distribution of the actual rates of oxygen uptake and that took account only of certain features of their relative magnitudes. The test described is often termed *distribution-free*. Perhaps the epithet seems strange in association with

87

a method that so plainly uses the binomial distribution; the binomial properties arise, however, solely from the independence of results from different pairs of rats and there is no appeal to a Normal or other distribution of measurements.

Several alternative distribution-free tests of significance have been proposed for the situation of Experiment THREE. One may number the rats from 1 to 32 for convenience of identification, and then write these numbers in order from the rat with the largest rate of oxygen uptake to the rat with the smallest. On the null hypothesis that the treatment A has no effect, each of the possible 32! (or more generally $n!$) orders has the same probability of occurring; the probability for every order is therefore

$$1/32!$$

and of course different orders are mutually exclusive (section 3.4). If treatment A in reality increases the rate of uptake (relative to D) rats on A will tend to appear early in the recorded order, and if it decreases the rate they will appear late. A test of significance can be constructed by counting how many of the possible orders are at least as extreme as the order recorded for the experiment in respect of showing a predominance of rats on treatment A at the beginning or at the end of the list. If there are S such orders, then

$$S/32!$$

is the probability to be compared with 0·05 (or other chosen level) to give the significance test. The phrase 'at least as extreme' conceals a need for a criterion for deciding which of two orders is the more extreme and alternative arbitrary rules on this lead to alternative forms of test (A38–A43). The subject will not be pursued further here.

8.3   THEOREMS ON LINEAR FUNCTIONS

Although distribution-free methods are simple in concept, the under-lying theory is complicated and often involves laborious calculations. Experimental scientists seldom like to use methods that take little account of the actual magnitudes of measurements they have laboriously made. Extensions of the ideas of Chapter 6 are therefore required. Whereas that chapter employed theory pertaining to the distribution of a mean of observations, the need now is to discuss differences between means of two distinct series of observations. Four more theorems can be stated.

THEOREM III

If x_i is a randomly selected observation from a distribution with mean ξ_i and variance σ_i^2, for each of $i = 1, 2, \ldots, n$, and if a_i is an associated arbitrary numerical constant, then the variate

$$X = \sum_{i=1}^{n} a_i x_i \tag{8.2}$$

has as its mean and variance

$$\xi_X = \sum a_i \xi_i, \tag{8.3}$$

$$\sigma_X^2 = \sum a_i^2 \sigma_i^2. \tag{8.4}$$

The Theorem is easily proved with the aid of (4.41) and (5.22); these can be applied to the expressions $a_i x_i$ and $M_X(\theta)$ multiplied out as far as the term in θ^2 (A44–A46).

THEOREM IV

If n_j observations are randomly and independently selected from a distribution with mean ξ_j, variance σ_j^2, for each of $j = 1, 2$, and $\bar{x}_1, \bar{x}_2$ are the arithmetic means of the two samples, then the variate

$$X = \bar{x}_2 - \bar{x}_1 \tag{8.5}$$

has as its mean and variance, under conditions of repeated sampling from the same distributions,

$$\xi_X = \xi_2 - \xi_1, \tag{8.6}$$

$$\sigma_X^2 = \frac{\sigma_1^2}{n_1} + \frac{\sigma_2^2}{n_2}. \tag{8.7}$$

This is a corollary of Theorem III. It is readily proved by writing $n_1 + n_2 = n$, and in Theorem III supposing the first n_1 values of x_i to have identical distributions corresponding to $j = 1$, the next n_2 to have identical distributions differing from the first and corresponding to $j = 2$. Then take

$$\left.\begin{array}{l} a_i = -\dfrac{1}{n_1} \quad \text{for } 1 \leqslant i \leqslant n_1, \\[2mm] a_i = \dfrac{1}{n_2} \quad \text{for } n_1 + 1 \leqslant i \leqslant n_1 + n_2. \end{array}\right\} \tag{8.8}$$

Although (8.3), (8.6) are intuitively obvious, (8.4) and (8.7) are not. Note particularly that the expectation of a difference between means of two samples is equal to the difference of the expectations; the variance of the difference, however, is equal to the *sum* of variances of the two means determined separately according to equation (5.28).

THEOREM V

Under the conditions of Theorem III or Theorem IV, if each x_i is Normally distributed then X is $N(\xi_X, \sigma_X^2)$.

The proof is essentially as for Theorem I, and formal presentation of it is left as an exercise for the student. Theorem I can be regarded as a special case of Theorem V in which every $a_i = 1/n$.

THEOREM VI

Under the conditions of Theorem IV

$$t = (X - \xi_X)/\sigma_X \tag{8.9}$$

has a distribution that tends to $N(0, 1)$ as $n_1, n_2 \to \infty$.

The proof can be obtained as in section 6.2 for Theorem II.

8.4 Form of Significance Test

Suppose that Experiment THREE were conducted with 10 rats on treatment A and 22 on treatment D, and in units of 10^{-9} litres per mg gave

$$\left. \begin{matrix} \bar{x}_1 = 59 \\ \bar{x}_2 = 52 \end{matrix} \right\} \tag{8.10}$$

as the means of the two series of observations. Then, if ξ_1, ξ_2 are written for the corresponding population means and σ_1^2, σ_2^2 for the corresponding variances, Theorem IV states that the difference,

$$\bar{x}_2 - \bar{x}_1 = -7 \tag{8.11}$$

can be regarded as a single observation from a distribution with mean as in (8.6) and variance

$$\sigma_X^2 = \frac{\sigma_1^2}{10} + \frac{\sigma_2^2}{22}. \tag{8.12}$$

Moreover, if the distributions of the original observations are Normal or not very different from Normal, Theorems V and VI show that the distribution of $\bar{x}_1 - \bar{x}_2$ will be exactly or approximately Normal.

No more can be done in the absence of all knowledge of σ_1^2, σ_2^2. As will be seen later (sections 10.6, 10.7), the practical procedure involves estimation of variance from the data. The logic can be illustrated here by supposing σ_1^2, σ_2^2 known, an unlikely state of affairs but an assumption that permits presentation of one new point at a time (cf. section 6.6). Suppose

$$\left. \begin{matrix} \sigma_1^2 = 100, \\ \sigma_2^2 = 132, \end{matrix} \right\} \tag{8.13}$$

are known. Consequently, by (8.12),

$$\sigma_X^2 = 10+6 = 16. \tag{8.14}$$

A null hypothesis that treatment A does not change the mean rate of oxygen uptake may be written

$$\xi_X = 0. \tag{8.15}$$

On this hypothesis, -7 (the observed difference in means) is to be regarded as an observation from $N(0, 16)$, and by Theorem VI

$$t = \frac{-7-0}{\sqrt{16}} = -1 \cdot 75 \tag{8.16}$$

is distributed approximately as $N(0, 1)$. Reference to Table 6.1 shows that for a double-tailed significance test (sections 6.6, 6.7) the probability that a value of $|t|$ as large as or larger than this occurs by chance is slightly smaller than 0·10 (more exactly, about 0·08); this would not usually be regarded as serious evidence against the null hypothesis.

8.5 PROBABILITY LIMITS

The theory may be applied to other null hypotheses which specify other values for ξ_X. Exactly the same logic as in section 6.8 leads to the statement that any ξ_X satisfying

$$\left| \frac{\bar{x}_2 - \bar{x}_1 - \xi_X}{\sigma_X} \right| \leqslant 1 \cdot 960 \tag{8.17}$$

will not be rejected by a significance test at probability 0·05. With the numerical values in section 8.4, this becomes

$$\left| \frac{-7 - \xi_X}{4} \right| \leqslant 1 \cdot 960.$$

Limits derived from this inequality are

$$-7 - 4 \times 1 \cdot 960 \leqslant \xi_X \leqslant -7 + 4 \times 1 \cdot 960 \tag{8.18}$$

or

$$-14 \cdot 8 \leqslant \xi_X \leqslant 0 \cdot 8. \tag{8.19}$$

These values, $-14\cdot8$ and $+0\cdot8$, are fiducial and confidence limits to $(\xi_2 - \xi_1)$, the difference in population means, at the probability 0·95. Similarly, at a probability 0·999 the limits are

$$-7 - 4 \times 3 \cdot 291 = -20 \cdot 2$$

and

$$-7 + 4 \times 3 \cdot 291 = 6 \cdot 2.$$

The conclusion that the population mean for treatment A exceeds that for D by an amount lying between such a pair of limits may be stated with an assurance represented by the probability used in calculating the limits.

8.6   DESIGN OF EXPERIMENT THREE

In preparing to conduct Experiment THREE, the investigator has to decide how many of the animals available for use shall be allotted to each treatment, subject to the constraint that the total shall not exceed n (or 32). This choice does not affect ξ_1, ξ_2 but can greatly influence σ_X^2. If no other factors influence his decision, he will naturally wish to minimise

$$\sigma_X^2 = \frac{\sigma_1^2}{n_1} + \frac{\sigma_2^2}{n_2} \tag{8.7}$$

subject to the condition

$$n_1 + n_2 = n. \tag{8.1}$$

(Obviously nothing can be gained by having $n_1 + n_2 < n$, since σ_X^2 can always be reduced by increasing either of the n_i until equality is attained.) By the argument in (A47–A49), the minimum is achieved when

$$\left. \begin{array}{l} n_1 = \dfrac{n\sigma_1}{\sigma_1 + \sigma_2}, \\[3mm] n_2 = \dfrac{n\sigma_2}{\sigma_1 + \sigma_2}. \end{array} \right\} \tag{8.20}$$

In practice, σ_1 and σ_2 will often be nearly equal or there will be no advance information on which is the larger. This reasoning suggests that most commonly

$$n_1 = n_2 = \tfrac{1}{2}n \tag{8.21}$$

will be a wise choice. Additional argument for (8.21) will appear in section 11.6.

Occasionally, choice of n_1, n_2 may be restricted by other considerations. Availability of experimental facilities may impose a maximum on n_1 smaller than $\tfrac{1}{2}n$, or other special considerations may indicate the desirability of having n_1 substantially smaller or substantially larger than n_2. When $\sigma_1 = \sigma_2$, the behaviour of σ_X^2 is determined by the factor

$$\frac{1}{n_1} + \frac{1}{n_2}; \tag{8.22}$$

in fact, moderate departures from the rule (8.21) have only a slight effect on this factor, as may be seen from Table 8.1, and a small increase in the total number of animals used would compensate adequately. However, the merits of symmetry implied by $n_1 = n_2$ are often important in other ways.

TABLE 8.1

Illustration of the behaviour of the expression (8.22) with n = 32

n_1	n_2	$\frac{1}{n_1} + \frac{1}{n_2}$	Ratio to minimum
4	28	0·2857	0·438
6	26	0·2051	0·609
8	24	0·1667	0·750
10	22	0·1455	0·859
12	20	0·1333	0·938
14	18	0·1270	0·984
16	16	0·1250	1·000
18	14	0·1270	0·984

EXERCISES

8.1 Write out a full proof of Theorem V.

8.2 Present a proof of Theorem VI analogous to that for Theorem II in section 6.2.

8.3 Suppose that the S.D. of systolic blood pressure is known to be 15 mm between healthy adult males and 20 mm between sufferers from a certain disease. A random sample of 79 healthy men has a mean blood pressure of 121 mm and a random sample of 11 with the disease has a mean of 137 mm. If Normal distributions can be assumed, what inferences can be drawn about any association between disease and blood pressure?

8.4 Under the conditions of Exercise 8.3, suppose that the same total of 90 men were equally divided between healthy and diseased, and the mean blood pressures were still 121 mm, 137 mm. Recompute the arithmetic for your inferences. Suppose that the total of 90 had been divided in accordance with equation (8.20): recompute.

8.5 An entomologist plans to study the difference in wing span between specimens of a butterfly caught at sea level and specimens of the same species caught on slopes at 1000 ft. He is satisfied that the variance of wing span is the same in both places, and wants to plan his work so as to minimise the variance of the difference between the estimated mean wing spans. If capturing one butterfly at sea level on average takes U minutes, and capturing one at 1000 ft on average takes V minutes, how many should the entomologist catch in each place in order to use a total time of W minutes to best advantage? By what factor will the variance of the difference be increased if

  (*i*) he chooses to catch equal numbers in each place, *or*
  (*ii*) he spends equal times catching in each place,

in either case maintaining a total time of W minutes?

Chapter 9

s^2, χ^2, AND t

9.1 Estimation of Parameters

The test of significance in section 8.4 and subsequent calculations were made possible only by regarding σ_1^2, σ_2^2 as known quantities. This is seldom realistic and often wholly impracticable: if the mean of a distribution is under discussion, the variance is unlikely to be already known.

Previous similar research may indeed have provided some indication of the magnitude of a variance, but conditions in two different experiments or sets of observations are rarely so alike that an exact value would be trustworthy. However, the individual measurements in the current research contain usable information on the variance, and this must now be discussed. In (8.10), only the means for the rats on the two treatments were stated. However, the rates of oxygen uptake for single rats, the basic observations of the experiment, can be used in calculating estimates of variance; the statistical procedures of sections 8.4, 8.5 must then be modified to permit replacement of σ^2 by its estimate.

The idea of estimation was introduced in section 3.8, and forms the main subject of Chapter 12, but a little more must be said here. Suppose that x_1, x_2, ..., x_n are n independent random observations from a distribution (not necessarily Normal) with mean ξ and variance σ^2. By definition

$$E(x_i) = \xi. \tag{9.1}$$

If as usual $\bar{x}$ is defined to be the arithmetic mean of the sample (it is of course a statistic in the sense of section 3.8),

$$\bar{x} = \sum_{i=1}^{n} x_i/n, \tag{9.2}$$

then by (5.26)

$$E(\bar{x}) = \xi. \tag{9.3}$$

One may speak of $\bar{x}$ as an *estimator* of ξ, using the word estimator for the mathematical function or rule of procedure from which a particular value, the *estimate*, is calculated in respect of one body of numerical data. By virtue of (9.3), $\bar{x}$ is described as an *unbiased* estimator of ξ: the exact meaning of the adjective is explained in section 12.4, but in brief it may be understood in the sense of being on average correct.

The property of unbiasedness is not unique; for example, a randomly chosen x_i is also an unbiased estimator of ξ. Indeed, it is not always an especially desirable property, but it is relevant to this chapter as well as being an easily comprehended idea. Often it needs reinforcement by other properties before the estimator can be regarded as optimal for the parameter. Within this chapter, such points are not discussed and unbiased estimators introduced are in fact optimal in other respects.

9.2   VARIANCE ESTIMATION

Procedures for the estimation of a variance are easy but less obvious than for a mean. With the x_i defined as in section 9.1, by definition

$$E[(x_i - \xi)^2] = \sigma^2. \tag{9.4}$$

Therefore, the expression

$$U = \Sigma(x_i - \xi)^2/n \tag{9.5}$$

is an unbiased estimator of σ^2. It is useless unless ξ is known. A natural step is to replace ξ by *its* estimator, $\bar{x}$; the function

$$V = \Sigma(x_i - \bar{x})^2/n \tag{9.6}$$

might seem a candidate for consideration.

Look first at the numerator of V, and apply the distributive rule for expectations, (4.19):

$$E[\Sigma(x_i - \bar{x})^2] = E[\Sigma(x_i - \xi - \bar{x} + \xi)^2]$$

$$= E[\Sigma(x_i - \xi)^2] - 2E[\Sigma(x_i - \xi)(\bar{x} - \xi)] + E[\Sigma(\bar{x} - \xi)^2]$$

$$= n\sigma^2 - 2n(\sigma^2/n) + n(\sigma^2/n) \quad \text{by (A50–A52)}$$

$$= (n-1)\sigma^2. \tag{9.7}$$

Hence

$$E(V) = (n-1)\sigma^2/n, \tag{9.8}$$

so that V is biased as an estimator of σ^2. However, simple adjustment leads to an unbiased estimator. Write

$$s^2 = \frac{\Sigma(x_i - \bar{x})^2}{n-1}; \tag{9.9}$$

by (9.7),
$$E(s^2) = \sigma^2, \tag{9.10}$$
so that s^2 is unbiased.

Hereafter s^2 is used always with the meaning of (9.9) or a generalisation of this, in accordance with the general practice of statisticians. A few statisticians, including authors of one or two textbooks, prefer to work with V of (9.6), which *they* denote by s^2. There is no absolute objection to the use of such a biased estimator, provided that appropriate adjustments are made in the presentation of theory. All that follows could be written in terms of V, by insertion of the factor $n/(n-1)$ in various places, but many formulae then assume more complicated shapes. The careless reader may be confused if he reads one text that adopts the present convention and another that denotes V by s^2. Numerically, s^2 and V are almost equal when n is large.

9.3   NOTE ON CALCULATION

The quantity $\sum (x_i - \bar{x})^2$ often must be calculated. Note the identity (A53)
$$\sum (x_i - \bar{x})^2 = \sum x_i^2 - (\sum x_i)^2/n. \tag{9.11}$$

The left-hand side of (9.11) is convenient for algebraic theory; the *right-hand side is almost always preferable for arithmetic*, by pen and paper or by desk calculator, though not for a high-speed computer. The only exceptions are cases where n is small and $\sum x_i/n$ divides out perfectly.

If you do not believe this recommendation (and few people do when first they see it), take $n=7$ and use for the x_i any 7 integers whose total is not divisible by 7; with them, calculate each side of (9.11) separately. The alternative form
$$\sum (x_i - \bar{x})^2 = \sum x_i^2 - n\bar{x}^2 \tag{9.12}$$
is sometimes useful but more liable to inaccuracies in consequence of the rounding of decimals. A minor variant that also has practical advantages for computation is
$$\sum (x_i - \bar{x})^2 = [n \sum x_i^2 - (\sum x_i)^2] \div n. \tag{9.13}$$

An obvious generalisation may expedite arithmetic, especially when no mechanical aids are available. For an arbitrary constant, a,
$$\sum (x_i - \bar{x})^2 = \sum [(x_i - a) - (\bar{x} - a)]^2$$
$$= \sum (x_i - a)^2 - (\sum x_i - na)^2/n \tag{9.14}$$

by (9.11). If all values of x_i lay between 1205 and 1277, for example, subtraction of 1200 from each before applying (9.11) and calculating $\sum (x_i - \bar{x})^2$ could save time; with the more sophisticated machinery, this step is seldom worth while and may introduce risks of error or delays that are absent from more direct computation.

A quantity of the form of that in (9.11) is termed a *sum of squares of deviations from a mean* or, where no ambiguity is likely to arise, simply a *sum of squares*.

9.4   THE GAMMA DISTRIBUTION

The factorial function, defined by

$$k! = k(k-1)(k-2)\ldots 3.2.1 \qquad (9.15)$$

for any positive integer k, is familiar to all mathematicians. It arises very frequently in formulae connected with permutations and combinations, and therefore appears in many expressions for probabilities associated with discrete variates.

In other branches of mathematics, a function known as the *gamma function* is so important that it has been much studied and tabulated. It is defined by

$$\Gamma(w) = \int_0^\infty z^{w-1} e^{-z} dz. \qquad (9.16)$$

For every real $w > 0$, this integral converges and takes a finite value. Despite its importance, many students of mathematics seem not to be introduced to it until late in their careers.

However, statisticians need the gamma function for a number of fairly elementary purposes. One reason is that, perhaps rather surprisingly, it represents a generalisation of the factorial function. By simple integration

$$\Gamma(1) = 1, \qquad (9.17)$$

and also by simple proof (A54)

$$\Gamma(w+1) = w\Gamma(w). \qquad (9.18)$$

Hence for every positive integer

$$k! = \Gamma(k+1), \qquad (9.19)$$

and the gamma function generalises the factorial to non-integer argument. Some authors indeed will write $(w-1)!$ in place of $\Gamma(w)$ even when w is non-integral.

Additional notes on the gamma function are inserted in the Appendix (A54–A55). Evidently

$$f(z) = z^{w-1} e^{-z}/\Gamma(w) \qquad (9.20)$$

satisfies the conditions for being a p.d.f. over the range $0 < z < \infty$, and this is known as a *gamma distribution*.

9.5 DISTRIBUTION OF s^2

One example of the derivation of the probability distribution of a function of a set of observations has already arisen. In section 5.5, the m.g.f. of the arithmetic mean of a series of independent observations was obtained in terms of the m.g.f. of the parent distribution from which they were randomly selected; in section 5.8, the special case of the Normal distribution was discussed (cf. Theorem I).

Processes of this kind are very important, and constitute a standard group of problems of statistical theory. One of these is the derivation of the distribution of s^2, which here can be considered only under the condition that the x_i are randomly and independently selected from the distribution $N(\xi, \sigma^2)$. The first step is to examine the distribution of $(x-\xi)^2$, for any one observation. By (4.39)

$$M_{(x-\xi)^2}(\theta) = \int_{-\infty}^{\infty} \frac{1}{\sigma\sqrt{(2\pi)}} \exp\left[\theta(x-\xi)^2 - \frac{(x-\xi)^2}{2\sigma^2}\right] dx$$

$$= (1 - 2\sigma^2\theta)^{-\frac{1}{2}} \qquad (9.21)$$

as proved in (A57). Consequently, by (5.22),

$$M_{\Sigma(x_i-\xi)^2}(\theta) = (1 - 2\sigma^2\theta)^{-n/2}. \qquad (9.22)$$

With U as defined by equation (9.5), (5.25) gives

$$M_U(\theta) = \left(1 - \frac{2\sigma^2\theta}{n}\right)^{-n/2}. \qquad (9.23)$$

The m.g.f. of U has been found first because the proof is simpler than for that of s^2 yet, as will be seen, the result is of much the same form. Insertion of ξ for a in (9.14) gives

$$\Sigma(x_i-\xi)^2 = \Sigma(x_i-\bar{x})^2 + n(\bar{x}-\xi)^2. \qquad (9.24)$$

Now $\bar{x}$ is distributed as $N(\xi, \sigma^2/n)$, by (5.46), and therefore by (9.21)

$$M_{(\bar{x}-\xi)^2}(\theta) = \left(1 - \frac{2\sigma^2\theta}{n}\right)^{-\frac{1}{2}}. \qquad (9.25)$$

Hence by (4.41)

$$M_{n(\bar{x}-\xi)^2}(\theta) = (1-2\sigma^2\theta)^{-\frac{1}{2}}, \qquad (9.26)$$

so that $n(\bar{x}-\xi)^2$ has exactly the same distribution as any one $(x_i-\xi)^2$. Taken in conjunction with (9.24), this suggests that $\sum(x_i-\bar{x})^2$ may be distributed as is the sum of $(n-1)$ independent variates of the form $(x-\xi)^2$, each having the m.g.f. in (9.21). At present, this statement simply has the status of an intelligent guess consistent with (9.22), (9.24)–(9.26). However, it can be shown that the two terms on the right-hand side of (9.24) are independently distributed (in the sense of section 3.5); consequently (5.21) requires that, in appropriate notation,

$$M_{\sum(x_i-\bar{x})^2}(\theta) = (1-2\sigma^2\theta)^{-(n-1)/2}, \qquad (9.27)$$

whence

$$M_{s^2}(\theta) = \left(1 - \frac{2\sigma^2\theta}{n-1}\right)^{-(n-1)/2}. \qquad (9.28)$$

A formal proof is given in the Appendix (A58–A68).

This m.g.f. is easily shown to be essentially that of a gamma distribution. If z has the p.d.f. (9.20) and c is an arbitrary constant, cz has the m.g.f.

$$M_{cz}(\theta) = \int_0^\infty z^{w-1} e^{-z(1-c\theta)} dz / \Gamma(w)$$

$$= (1-c\theta)^{-w} \qquad (9.29)$$

by an obvious change of variable and use of (9.16). Identification of (9.28) with (9.29) then shows that s^2 has the distribution of $2\sigma^2 z/(n-1)$ with $w = \frac{1}{2}(n-1)$. Writing in (9.20)

$$z = \frac{(n-1)s^2}{2\sigma^2} \qquad (9.30)$$

and not forgetting that

$$dz = \frac{n-1}{2\sigma^2} d(s^2), \qquad (9.31)$$

the p.d.f. for s^2 is seen to be

$$f(s^2) = \left(\frac{n-1}{2\sigma^2}\right)^{\frac{1}{2}(n-1)} (s^2)^{\frac{1}{2}(n-3)} \exp\left[-\frac{(n-1)s^2}{2\sigma^2}\right] / \Gamma\left(\frac{n-1}{2}\right). \qquad (9.32)$$

Note that the variate whose distribution is here presented is s^2; if the p.d.f. for s is required, one must write

$$f(s^2) d(s^2) = f(s^2) 2s \, ds, \qquad (9.33)$$

and therefore the p.d.f. for s is (9.32) multiplied by $2s$.

Of course (9.28) can be expanded as a power series in θ and the moments of s^2 obtained. The first obviously confirms that

$$E(s^2) = \sigma^2. \tag{9.10}$$

Evidently (9.32) represents a family of distributions distinguished by their values of n, where n is an integer greater than unity. The definition (9.9) suggests a special role for $(n-1)$ rather than n, and this is known as the number of *degrees of freedom* on which s^2 is based. The name arises from a geometrical representation of the problem, and the reason for it will be made clearer by section 9.6. It may be regarded as the number of independent items of information on the deviations of single observations from $\bar{x}$; when $\bar{x}$ is fixed, knowledge of any $(n-1)$ values of x_i serves to determine the remaining one. If $n=1$, the observations convey no information on variance, and correspondingly there are 0 degrees of freedom. The abbreviation *d.f.* is generally used.

*9.6   An Alternative Proof

The distribution of s^2 is so important that presentation of an entirely different proof is justifiable. A proof based on geometrical argument in n dimensions has historical interest, because it was devised by R. A. Fisher (1890–1962), whose major contributions to statistical theory and practice have been so largely responsible for the close association of statistical method with scientific research and technology in many fields. This proof is characteristic of his highly original mind, which operated rapidly and intuitively by geometrical analogy, leaving the detail of analytical rigour for subsequent study. It makes reference to the analogues of circles and spheres in n-dimensional space. The only property needed is that the 'volume' of an n-dimensional hypersphere of radius r is proportional to r^n. This is well known for $n=2$ and $n=3$, and the general result will be intuitively obvious to most students of mathematics, but for those who find the idea difficult the Appendix contains more explanation (A69–A74).

Regard the n observations $(x_1, x_2, \ldots, x_n)$ as the co-ordinates of a point X in n-dimensional space. Let M be the point with co-ordinates $(\xi, \xi, \ldots, \xi)$. Join M to the origin, O, and let p be the (unique) hyperplane (of dimensions $n-1$) through X to which OM is perpendicular. Let OM meet p at P. Fig. 9.1 illustrates this situation for $n=2$, visualisation for $n=3$ is easy, and a little imagination should aid the general concept!

Now the line OM is the locus of all points for which

$$x_1 = x_2 = \ldots = x_n, \tag{9.34}$$

and, on any hyperplane perpendicular to OM, $\Sigma\, x_i$ is constant. There-fore P is the point $(\bar{x}, \bar{x}, ..., \bar{x})$. By generalisations of Pythogoras's theorem,

$$MX^2 = MP^2 + PX^2, \tag{9.35}$$

$$MX^2 = \Sigma\, (x_i - \xi)^2, \tag{9.36}$$

$$MP^2 = n(\bar{x} - \xi)^2, \tag{9.37}$$

$$PX^2 = \Sigma\, (x_i - \bar{x})^2 = (n-1)\, s^2. \tag{9.38}$$

Hence (9.35) is equivalent to (9.24).

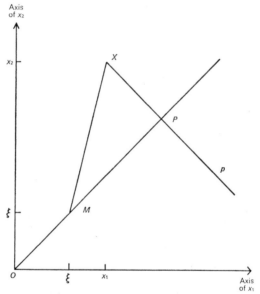

Fig. 9.1. The geometrical representation (§9.6) with $n=2$; p is a line perpendicular to the line OM, passing through X and intersecting OM at the point P.

As in (A60), the probability that observation i lies in the interval $(x_i, x_i + dx_i)$ for all i can be written

$$\left(\frac{1}{\sigma\sqrt{(2\pi)}}\right)^n \exp\left[-\frac{\Sigma\, (x_i - \xi)^2}{2\sigma^2}\right] dx_1\, dx_2 \ldots dx_n$$

$$= \left(\frac{1}{\sigma\sqrt{(2\pi)}}\right)^n \exp\left[-\frac{(n-1)\, s^2 + n(\bar{x} - \xi)^2}{2\sigma^2}\right] dx_1\, dx_2 \ldots dx_n. \tag{9.39}$$

The distribution of s^2 will be obtained if this expression can be averaged over all $x_1, x_2, ..., x_n$ for which s^2 is constant. A first step is to change the variables in which the differential element is expressed, introducing s^2 as one of these and subsequently integrating over the whole range of all the others. For example, the new set of variables might be s^2, $\bar{x}$, x_3, x_4, ..., x_n, and integration will then be over $(-\infty, \infty)$ for all except the first; the result will be $f(s^2)\,d(s^2)$, where $f(s^2)$ is the p.d.f.

The element of hypervolume in (9.39) can be regarded as compounded of an elemental increment in the direction OP, $d\bar{x}$, and an element of $(n-1)$ dimensional hypervolume in the hyperplane p perpendicular to OP (think of 2, 3 dimensions). Within p, $\bar{x}$ is constant and the p.d.f. will be constant when s^2 also is constant, as is evident from (9.39). Now the region of constant s^2 within p consists of all points, Q, in p for which PQ is fixed and therefore equal to PX. Moreover p, a space perpendicular to a line in n dimensions, has $(n-1)$ dimensions (again think of 2, 3 dimensions); therefore, the region of constant s^2 is the surface of a hypersphere of radius PX in $(n-1)$ dimensions. The volume of this hypersphere is proportional to $(PX)^{n-1}$ or to s^{n-1}; consequently the element of hypervolume for constant s is proportional to $s^{n-2}ds$, the differential of s^{n-1}. The summation of probability over the surface of the hypersphere is equivalent to the integration over all variates except s^2, $\bar{x}$. The joint distribution of s^2 and $\bar{x}$ may now be expressed as

$$\text{constant} \times \exp\left[-\frac{(n-1)s^2 + n(\bar{x}-\xi)^2}{2\sigma^2}\right] s^{n-2}\,ds\,d\bar{x}$$
$$= [\text{constant} \times e^{-(n-1)s^2/(2\sigma^2)}\, s^{n-2}\,ds] \times [\text{constant} \times e^{-n(\bar{x}-\xi)^2/(2\sigma^2)}\,d\bar{x}].$$
$$(9.40)$$

Writing it in this form displays the second factor, containing $\bar{x}$ but not s, as the distribution of $\bar{x}$ (Theorem I). The first factor contains s but not $\bar{x}$; since the joint probability is expressible in the form of this product, by a converse of (3.8) the first factor must be the probability that s lies within an interval of width ds. Use of

$$d(s^2) = 2s\,ds \qquad (9.41)$$

permits this to be written

$$\text{constant} \times (s^2)^{(n-3/2)}\, e^{-(n-1)s^2/(2\sigma^2)}\,d(s^2). \qquad (9.42)$$

Comparison with (9.20), or integration and equation to 1, then enables the constant to be evaluated and agreement with (9.32) is confirmed.

9.7 Use of the s^2 Distribution

The p.d.f. (9.32) represents a family of distributions distinguished by the numbers of degrees of freedom. An integral of the function is needed for tests of significance. By analogy with section 6.5, define the function $Hp(v_0)$ as the probability that

$$\frac{s^2}{\sigma^2} \geqslant v_0; \qquad (9.43)$$

the symbol is chosen to indicate the *Helmert probability*, after the astronomer and mathematician who first studied the distribution. Here s^2 is as defined earlier, v_0 is an arbitrary positive quantity, and the distribution has f degrees of freedom ($f \geqslant 1$); the notation symbolises the variance probability associated with the ratio v_0. The change of variable expressed by

$$s^2 = \sigma^2 v \qquad (9.44)$$

leads to

$$Hp(v_0) = \frac{1}{\Gamma(\frac{1}{2}f)} \left(\frac{f}{2\sigma^2}\right)^{\frac{1}{2}f} \int_{v_0\sigma^2}^{\infty} (s^2)^{\frac{1}{2}f-1} e^{-fs^2/(2\sigma^2)} d(s^2)$$

$$= \frac{(\frac{1}{2}f)^{\frac{1}{2}f}}{\Gamma(\frac{1}{2}f)} \int_{v_0}^{\infty} v^{\frac{1}{2}f-1} e^{-\frac{1}{2}fv} dv. \qquad (9.45)$$

Evidently the integral is of the gamma function type. Table 9.1 contains numerical values in a form analogous to that of Table 6.1, and greater detail is available in many collections of statistical tables. The method of construction from the integral need not be discussed here.

TABLE 9.1

Values of s^2/σ^2 for prescribed values of $Hp(s^2/\sigma^2)$ and various numbers of degrees of freedom

$Hp(s^2/\sigma^2)$ $f=$ 1	2	3	4	5	10	20	30
0·1 2·71	2·30	2·08	1·94	1·85	1·60	1·42	1·34
0·05 3·84	3·00	2·60	2·37	2·21	1·83	1·57	1·46
0·01 6·64	4·60	3·78	3·32	3·02	2·32	1·88	1·70

9.8   THE χ^2 STATISTIC

In statistical practice, a quantity defined as

$$\chi^2 = \frac{fs^2}{\sigma^2} \text{ with } f \text{ degrees of freedom}, \qquad (9.46)$$

or in the notation of section 9.5

$$\chi^2 = \sum (x_i - \bar{x})^2/\sigma^2 \text{ with } (n-1) \text{ degrees of freedom}, \qquad (9.47)$$

is more commonly used, largely for historical reasons. A table like Table 9.1 but with each entry multiplied by f is the basis of many procedures known as 'χ^2 tests'; Table 9.1 itself can be used just as satisfactorily. For example, a value of s^2 calculated from a sample can be compared with a theoretical σ^2 in a test of significance with a logical pattern like that of section 6.6.

9.9 AN EXAMPLE

Experience has shown that certain components of an electronic system, several of which are in use simultaneously, vary in their useful lives in such a way that the frequency distribution is Normal with mean 28 days, S.D. 2 days. A slight change is made in the method of manufacture with the aim of increasing the mean life. There is a fear that the variability may also have been increased, and this would be a serious disadvantage. A random sample of six from a batch of the new components is tested, and these remain usable for 29, 33, 36, 28, 27, 34 days. Is there clear evidence of an increase in variance?

Originally the distribution was $N(28, 4)$. The null hypothesis to be considered is that the six observations come from a distribution $N(\xi, 4)$, where ξ is unknown although the manufacturer's intention was that it should exceed 28. For the sample,

$$\bar{x} = (29+33+36+28+27+34)/6 = 187/6 = 31 \cdot 2;$$

the question whether this significantly exceeds 28 is asked as Example 10.1. An estimate of variance for the new components is given by (9.9), (9.11):

$$(n-1)s^2 = 29^2+33^2+36^2+28^2+27^2+34^2-\frac{187^2}{6}$$

$$= 5895 \cdot 00 - 5828 \cdot 17$$

$$= 66 \cdot 83.$$

Therefore

$$s^2 = 66 \cdot 83/5 = 13 \cdot 37$$

with 5 degrees of freedom. From the null hypothesis,

$$\frac{s^2}{\sigma^2} = \frac{13 \cdot 37}{4}$$

$$= 3 \cdot 34.$$

which exceeds all the entries in Table 9.1 for $f=5$: if the null hypothesis is true, the probability of a sample of 6 showing variability at least as great as this is less than 0·01. One may reasonably conclude that the null hypothesis is untrue, and that the variance for the new components exceeds 4.

9.10 DISTRIBUTION OF t

Another important distribution must now be introduced. If x is $N(\xi, \sigma^2)$, as is now well known (sections 5.3, 5.8),

$$\frac{x-\xi}{\sigma}$$

is $N(0, 1)$. Suppose that σ, as usual unknown, is replaced by an estimate s, calculated by (9.9) or an equivalent formula from some *independent* observations known also to have σ^2 as their variance. The reason for this seemingly odd supposition will become clear later. Write

$$t = \frac{x-\xi}{s}, \qquad (9.48)$$

where s has, say, f degrees of freedom. The distribution of t will not be $N(0, 1)$, and intuition suggests that the additional uncertainty introduced by s will increase the dispersion relative to $N(0, 1)$. If f increases indefinitely, s will approach σ, and convergence of the distribution to $N(0, 1)$ may be expected.

Independence of the distributions of x, s^2 (cf. sections 9.5, 9.6) means that the probability of a pair of values of these quantities lying in intervals of width dx, $d(s^2)$ can be written

$$\text{constant} \times \exp\left[-\frac{(x-\xi)^2}{2\sigma^2}\right](s^2)^{\frac{1}{2}f-1}\exp\left[-\frac{fs^2}{2\sigma^2}\right]dx\,d(s^2). \qquad (9.49)$$

Replacement of x by $(st+\xi)$, from (9.48), and integration over the range of s^2 (A75–A82) gives as the p.d.f. for t

$$\text{constant} \times \left(1+\frac{t^2}{f}\right)^{-\frac{1}{2}(f+1)}. \qquad (9.50)$$

Note that

$$\left(1+\frac{t^2}{f}\right)^{-\frac{1}{2}(f+1)} \rightarrow e^{-\frac{1}{2}t^2} \quad \text{as } f \rightarrow \infty, \qquad (9.51)$$

so that the distribution of t tends to $N(0, 1)$ as f becomes large.

The use of the symbol t to represent a quantity such as (9.48) has long been standard statistical usage. Because the Normal distribution can be regarded as a limiting form of the t distribution, the same symbol has been used in section 6.2 and elsewhere. When distinction is essential,

$$t_{[f]}$$

can be used to denote a t with f degrees of freedom, and

$$t_\infty$$

will refer to the Normal distribution. The reason for interest in t will be made clear in Chapter 10.

9.11 THE DISTRIBUTION FUNCTION OF t

The distribution function for $t_{[f]}$ is

$$F(T) = \int_{-\infty}^{T} f(t) \, dt, \qquad (9.52)$$

where $f(t)$ is given by (A82). This is analogous to (6.15) in representing the probability that a single random observation on t will be less than a specified T. Equation (9.52) replaces (6.15) and the argument of section 6.5 can be repeated. The function $Sp(t)$, a generalisation of $Gp(t)$, may be defined by

$$Sp(t_0) = Pr(t \geqslant t_0) = 1 - F(t_0), \qquad (9.53)$$

the analogy with (6.16), (6.18) being obvious. The symbol indicates the 'Student' probability, 'Student' being the pseudonym adopted by the statistician who first obtained the essential features of the distribution. With (9.52) in place of (6.15) and $Sp(t)$ replacing $Gp(t)$, equations (6.17), (6.19) remain true.

TABLE 9.2

Deviates of the t distribution for specified probabilities

$F(T)$	0·50	0·95	0·975	0·990	0·995	0·9995
$Sp(T)$	0·50	0·05	0·025	0·010	0·005	0·0005
$2Sp(T)$	1·00	0·10	0·050	0·020	0·010	0·0010
No. of d.f.						
2	0·000	2·920	4·303	6·965	9·925	31·598
4	0·000	2·132	2·776	3·747	4·604	8·610
6	0·000	1·943	2·447	3·143	3·707	5·959
8	0·000	1·860	2·306	2·896	3·355	5·041
10	0·000	1·812	2·228	2·764	3·169	4·587
15	0·000	1·753	2·131	2·602	2·947	4·073
20	0·000	1·725	2·086	2·528	2·845	3·850
40	0·000	1·684	2·021	2·423	2·704	3·551
∞	0·000	1·645	1·960	2·326	2·576	3·291

By appropriate numerical techniques, the integrals have been evaluated for many different values of f, the number of degrees of freedom. Extensive tables relating to $Sp(T)$ have been produced, so as to provide the appropriate generalisations of Table 6.1. For present purposes, the simple version in Table 9.2 will suffice; the convergence to the values in the last line, repeated from Table 6.1, is apparent. Of course $F(T)$ now represents the integral in (9.52) and not that in (6.15).

Practical use of the t distribution is so important that it deserves a separate chapter.

EXERCISES

9.1 For $n=11$, suppose values of x_i to be 32, 40, 39, 47, 34, 35, 49, 35, 41, 33, 38. Calculate $\sum (x_i - \bar{x})^2$ in four ways (to 2 places of decimals):

(i) find $\bar{x}$ and use the left-hand side of (9.11),
(ii) use the right-hand side of (9.11),
(iii) use (9.14) with $a=30$,
(iv) use (9.14) with $a=38$.

9.2 If $\sum x_i = 0$, $\sum y_i = 0$ ($i=1, 2, \ldots, n$) and b is defined by

$$b \sum x_i^2 = \sum x_i y_i,$$

prove that

$$\sum (y_i - bx_i)^2 = \sum y_i^2 - b \sum x_i y_i.$$

9.3 Write down the p.d.f. for U in equation (9.5), and for V in equation (9.6), on the assumption that x_i is $N(\xi, \sigma^2)$.

9.4 The variate x has the distribution $N(\xi, \sigma^2)$ and a single observation is 24·2. Find fiducial limits to ξ at probability 0·95 (cf. section 6.8, and adapt it using Table 9·2 where necessary) if

(i) $\sigma = 10·6$ is known;
(ii) σ is unknown, but from other evidence an estimate s^2 with 10 d.f. is known and gives $s=11·3$;
(iii) as (ii), but s^2 has 4 d.f.

9.5 Suppose that 16 independent observations of x as in Exercise 9.4 have a mean 24·2; obtain fiducial limits as before, assuming no additional information on σ^2 or s^2 available from variation between the 16 observations. (Consider the distribution of $\bar{x}$, and use what is known about σ^2 appropriately.)

9.6 With conditions as in Exercise 9.4, find the smallest value of σ^2 *not* rejected by a significance test at probability 0·05 for each situation in respect of s^2. These are single-tailed lower fiducial limits for σ^2 at probability 0·95. What additional tabulation in extension of Table 9.1 would be needed in order to obtain upper fiducial limits and double-tailed limits at this probability?

Chapter 10

USE OF t DISTRIBUTION AND GENERALISATIONS

10.1 INDEPENDENCE

The t distribution has been introduced (section 9.10) in relation to an observation from a Normal distribution and an estimate, s^2, of σ^2 from independent observations. The implication was, intentionally, that s^2 would be calculated from *different* observations having the *same* variance. Apparently this helps little with the problem of data such as those of section 6.6, where an inference about ξ is wanted from a value of $\bar{x}$ and the only information on σ^2 is that contained in the sample of observations from which $\bar{x}$ has been calculated.

The key lies in (9.24) and (9.40). The distribution of s^2 is independent of that of $\bar{x}$, even when both are calculated from the same n observations $x_1, x_2, \ldots, x_n$. The partitioning of $\sum (x_i - \xi)^2$ represented by (9.24) suggests this possibility. The proof lies in the fact that (9.40) has two factors; one is the p.d.f. of $\bar{x}$ which does not involve s^2, the other is a p.d.f. not involving $\bar{x}$ which from the manner of its derivation can relate only to the distribution of s^2. This is exactly the condition required for independence of the two distributions. Therefore the proof in section 9.10 remains valid, provided that s in that proof is suitably redefined. The distribution of $\bar{x}$ is $N(\xi, \sigma^2/n)$, and therefore the t distribution must be used with s^2/n as the estimated variance and $f = (n-1)$. In other words, equation (9.48) is modified to

$$t = (\bar{x} - \xi)\sqrt{(n)}/s, \tag{10.1}$$

where t has $(n-1)$ d.f.

10.2 USE OF THE t DISTRIBUTION

Equation (10.1) has the form of (6.9) except that s replaces σ. It can be employed similarly, provided that t is taken to have the right number of

110

degrees of freedom. If the distribution of x is strictly Normal, then (cf. Theorem I) t will have the p.d.f. in (9.50); if x is not strictly Normal, then (cf. Theorem II) t will approximate to having this p.d.f. for large n. Procedures based upon Theorems I, II can now be adapted for use with the t distribution, notably those of section 6.6.

This may be illustrated for the hypothetical values of x at the beginning of section 6.6. From them and equation (9.11),

$$\Sigma (x_i - \bar{x})^2 = 16^2 + 14^2 + (-4)^2 + \ldots + 10^2 - \frac{88^2}{16}$$

$$= 1944 - 484$$

$$= 1460. \tag{10.2}$$

Therefore, by (9.9), an estimate of σ^2 with 15 d.f. is

$$s^2 = \tfrac{1460}{15}$$

$$= 97 \cdot 33. \tag{10.3}$$

Hence

$$t = \frac{(5 \cdot 50 - \xi) \times 4}{\sqrt{97 \cdot 33}}$$

$$= (5 \cdot 50 - \xi)/2 \cdot 47 \tag{10.4}$$

may be taken to have the t distribution with 15 d.f.

The null hypothesis $\xi = 0$ gives

$$t = 2 \cdot 2, \tag{10.5}$$

which is just greater than the value $2 \cdot 13$ in Table 9.2 for 15 d.f. and a double-tailed probability $0 \cdot 05$. The conclusion therefore is that treatment A does affect the rate of oxygen uptake relative to treatment D; this is the conclusion that emerged from test of the same null hypothesis in section 6.6, but now dependence on any previous knowledge of σ^2 has been removed. In other respects, the logic is essentially the same.

Fiducial limits at a specified probability are obtainable from the obvious modification of equations (6.36):

$$\left.\begin{aligned}\xi_U &= \bar{x} + Ts/\sqrt{n} \\ \xi_L &= \bar{x} - Ts/\sqrt{n.}\end{aligned}\right\} \tag{10.6}$$

For probability $0 \cdot 95$, the appropriate T (with 15 d.f.; Table 9.2), is $2 \cdot 131$. Therefore

$$\left.\begin{aligned}\xi_U &= 5 \cdot 50 + 2 \cdot 131 \times 2 \cdot 47 = 10 \cdot 76, \\ \xi_L &= 5 \cdot 50 - 2 \cdot 131 \times 2 \cdot 47 = 0 \cdot 24,\end{aligned}\right\} \tag{10.7}$$

which are somewhat wider apart than the limits in (6.35) because estimation of σ^2 from only 15 d.f. requires appreciable increase in T. Similarly limits at probability 0·99 are 12·78 and −1·78.

10.3 ANOTHER NOTE ON CALCULATION

If any reader has doubted the wisdom of the advice in section 9.3 that the right-hand side of equation (9.11) is almost always the best way of calculating a sum of squares of deviations, he should obtain the result in (10.2) by any other arithmetical procedure that takes his fancy, for example

$$(16-5\cdot5)^2+(14-5\cdot5)^2+ \ldots +(20-5\cdot5)^2.$$

Retain sufficient arithmetical accuracy to verify that the result is *exactly* 1460!

10.4 STANDARD ERROR

In section 4.8, the name standard deviation was introduced for the square root of μ_2, a measure of the spread of observations in a distribution. When emphasis is placed on one observation or a mean of several as an estimate of an unknown population mean, the term *standard error* (S.E.) is often used. Commonly a standard deviation relates to a single observation, a standard error to a mean, but this is not an absolute distinction; wherever doubt is possible, the user of either term should *explicitly state of what quantity* he is quoting the S.D. or the S.E. If clarity is ensured in this way, the choice of name can often be regarded as a stylistic convenience. Both S.D. and S.E. are commonly used by statisticians, and avoidance of misunderstanding is important.

A numerical, or an algebraic, value for the S.E. is commonly introduced by the sign '$\pm$', read 'plus or minus'. Thus in section 6.6, where σ^2 is supposed known, one may state the mean of the observations as

$$5\cdot50 \pm 2\cdot50,$$

the second quantity being the standard error. In section 10.2, the estimated S.E. is obtained, and similarly the mean can be written

$$5\cdot50 \pm 2\cdot47.$$

This is a convenient shorthand for routine statement of a numerical value with a measure of its precision.

10.5 DEGREES OF FREEDOM

It is important to note that section 10.1 and the argument leading to it *permit* s^2, the variance estimate, to be based upon the $(n-1)$ d.f.

from the n observations that are averaged to give $\bar{x}$, but they do not require this. There are situations in which s^2 may be calculated from data other than those in $\bar{x}$ or from other data in addition to those in $\bar{x}$; s^2 will then have f degrees of freedom, a number usually exceeding $(n-1)$.

The number of degrees of freedom for t is *always* the number for the value of s^2 used, irrespective of whether s^2 has been calculated as in (9.9) or by some more general formula such as arises in the analysis of variance. Although t is often used with $(n-1)$ d.f., it is essential to realise that the true determinant of the d.f. is s^2 and not $\bar{x}$.

10.6   DIFFERENCE BETWEEN TWO MEANS

Just as the ideas of Chapter 6 have been extended to take account of estimation of variance, so also must be those of Chapter 8. In Theorems IV, V, VI, the true variance, σ_X^2, must be replaced by an estimate calculated from the data in such a way that the t distribution is still applicable. One new point of logic emerges in the formulation of the null hypothesis. If, as in section 8.4, the hypothesis is merely that

$$\xi_1 = \xi_2 \qquad (10.8)$$

within the framework of the model that the distributions of x_1, x_2 are $N(\xi_1, \sigma_1^2)$, $N(\xi_2, \sigma_2^2)$ respectively, two distinct variance estimates are required and in fact the t distribution cannot be used. A procedure can be devised, but special difficulties are involved. If instead the null hypothesis is that treatment A does not differ from D in its effect on the rate of oxygen uptake (cf. section 3.1), then within the same Normal framework the null hypothesis is stating that both distributions are $N(\xi, \sigma^2)$. There is now only one variance to be estimated, and as will be seen the t distribution can be used. The null hypothesis is equally appropriate to the experiment. Rejection of the null hypothesis after a test of statistical significance could be due to inequality of σ_1^2, σ_2^2 rather than of ξ_1, ξ_2, since either would constitute non-identity of the two distributions. An effect of treatment A that changed the variance of the observations without necessarily changing the mean would be intrinsically interesting. However, experience shows that in practice inequalities of variance are seldom great enough to cause this test to give the verdict 'significant', and rejection of the null hypothesis may usually be safely interpreted as a consequence of unequal means.

Suppose that observations consist of n_1 observations from one source, these being x_{1i} ($i = 1, 2, \ldots, n_1$), and n_2 observations from another source, these being x_{2i} ($i = 1, 2, \ldots, n_2$). Write $\sum\limits_{j}$ to denote summation over the n_j observations and $\bar{x}_j$ for the mean of these, so that

$$\bar{x}_1 = \sum_1 x_{1i}/n_1$$
$$= (x_{11} + x_{12} + \ldots + x_{1n_1})/n_1. \tag{10.9}$$

On the null hypothesis, evidently two distinct estimators of σ^2 can be formed, with $(n_1 - 1)$ and $(n_2 - 1)$ degrees of freedom respectively. How are these to be combined into a single estimator? Simple averaging might seem the obvious answer; it would scarcely be very sensible if n_1 were much larger than n_2 so that the first estimator was obviously much more trustworthy than the second. The correct procedure emerges from a formula analogous to (9.24):

$$\sum_1 (x_{1i} - \xi)^2 + \sum_2 (x_{2i} - \xi)^2$$
$$= \sum_1 (x_{1i} - \bar{x}_1)^2 + \sum_2 (x_{2i} - \bar{x}_2)^2 + \frac{n_1 n_2}{n_1 + n_2}(\bar{x}_1 - \bar{x}_2)^2 + (n_1 + n_2)(\bar{x} - \xi)^2, \tag{10.10}$$

where $\bar{x}$ is the general mean of all the observations:

$$\bar{x} = \frac{\sum\limits_1 x_{1i} + \sum\limits_2 x_{2i}}{n_1 + n_2} = \frac{n_1 \bar{x}_1 + n_2 \bar{x}_2}{n_1 + n_2}. \tag{10.11}$$

Equation (10.10) is proved in the Appendix (A83).

Now by arguments similar to those of Chapter 9, the four terms on the right-hand side of (10.10) may be proved independently distributed. Moreover, the joint distribution of all the $(n_1 + n_2)$ observations involves the left-hand side of (10.10) in a form closely analogous to the left-hand side of (9.39). Obviously by (9.7)

$$E\left[\sum_1 (x_{1i} - \bar{x}_1)^2 + \sum_2 (x_{2i} - \bar{x}_2)^2\right] = (n_1 + n_2 - 2)\sigma^2. \tag{10.12}$$

Therefore, by writing

$$s^2 = \frac{\sum\limits_1 (x_{1i} - \bar{x}_1)^2 + \sum\limits_2 (x_{2i} - \bar{x}_2)^2}{n_1 + n_2 - 2}, \tag{10.13}$$

the first two terms on the right of (10.10) become $(n_1 + n_2 - 2)s^2$. This may now be considered together with the third term on the right of (10.10) in a development of theory essentially the same as in sections 9.10, 10.1 to give

$$t = \frac{\bar{x}_2 - \bar{x}_1}{s}\Bigg/\sqrt{\left(\frac{n_1 n_2}{n_1 + n_2}\right)} \tag{10.14}$$

as a statistic that follows the t distribution with (n_1+n_2-2) d.f. The detail of proof will not be presented here; it follows very closely the pattern of Chapter 9, and indeed by a slightly more sophisticated approach the two can be made identical, but a full account would be tedious.

The form of (10.14) needs comment, especially in relation to section 8.3. If in (8.7) σ_1^2 and σ_2^2 are both put equal to σ^2, that equation becomes

$$\sigma_X^2 = \sigma^2 \left(\frac{1}{n_1}+\frac{1}{n_2}\right). \tag{10.15}$$

From (10.12), (10.13)

$$E(s^2) = \sigma^2. \tag{10.16}$$

Therefore σ_X^2 is estimated by

$$s_X^2 = s^2 \left(\frac{1}{n_1}+\frac{1}{n_2}\right), \tag{10.17}$$

and (10.14) may be rewritten

$$t = \frac{X}{s_X}, \tag{10.18}$$

where

$$X = \bar{x}_2 - \bar{x}_1. \tag{8.5}$$

A further generalisation follows easily by beginning with a null hypothesis that allows the two distributions to differ in mean but not in variance. This hypothesis might state that x_{1i}, x_{2i} have the distributions $N(\xi_1, \sigma^2)$, $N(\xi_2, \sigma^2)$ respectively. Then

$$t = \frac{X-(\xi_2-\xi_1)}{s_X}, \tag{10.19}$$

again with (n_1+n_2-2) d.f. Evidently (10.18) and (10.19) are related to (8.9) in the same way as is (10.1) to (6.9), the change simply being replacement of σ_X by an estimator that can be calculated from the data. The question of how to combine estimates of σ^2 from the two parts of the data has been answered incidentally: sums of squares are additive, as appears in (10.13). Any alternative combination would not lead to a statistic following the t distribution. This is in itself no more than a statement that the method implied by (10.13), (10.18), (10.19) is conveniently simple, but it can be proved to have important optimal properties.

Although the argument has been outlined rather briefly here, the reader ought to be able to see that the logical steps giving (10.1) and its distribution as a more practically useful development from (6.9) similarly give (10.19) and its distribution as a more practically useful development from (8.9), except that (10.19) also incorporates $\sigma_1^2 = \sigma_2^2$ into the null hypothesis. In each case, a statistic employing a known variance, σ^2, is replaced by one employing an estimate of this variance formed from an appropriate sum of squares of deviations. In each case, numerator and denominator of the statistic must have independent probability distributions, and formal proof of the independence is perhaps the most difficult step. In each case, the only other component of the statistic requiring comment is a multiple depending upon numbers of subjects or observations, this being the factor that converts variance per observation, σ^2, into the variance of the numerator of the statistic.

10.7 Numerical Example

Suppose that the numerical values for $\bar{x}_1$, $\bar{x}_2$ used as a hypothetical example in section 8.4 in fact arose as the means of the 10 and 22 observations presented in Table 10.1. The calculations for which the theory is

Table 10.1

Hypothetical values of x_{1i} and x_{2i} for Experiment THREE, in conformity with section 8.4

x_{1i} ($n_1 = 10$)	x_{2i} ($n_2 = 22$)	
67	64	69
79	41	57
54	58	62
52	55	43
59	50	59
48	52	40
62	38	49
52	59	33
57	70	62
60	40	67
	36	40

presented in section 10.6 can rapidly be built up from these data. They are summarised below in systematic arrangement. The reader is advised to adopt some such routine if he must analyse similar data at all frequently. A good routine reduces the risk of errors of copying or arithmetic as well as of method, expedites the computations, simplifies checking, and encourages clear presentation of results. The exact system to be chosen should depend on the mechanical aids available.

That described here is in principle suitable for pen-and-paper arithmetic and for most desk calculating machines, though the facilities of particular machines may encourage some modifications. A programme for a high-speed electronic computer might follow essentially the same pattern, but advantage may be taken of greater possibilities for conducting different parts of the calculations in parallel instead of in series and reading each datum once only. The calculations described here are indeed trivial for an electronic computer, but the adoption of efficient systematic practices even for simple arithmetic encourages good habits that should continue when either the mathematician or the statistician must undertake a major piece of computation.

The student will be wise to verify each step that follows; if he must work with pen and paper alone, he can reduce his labour substantially by first subtracting some convenient quantity from each entry in Table 10.1, but with a desk calculator to work with the data as they stand is probably quicker and safer. By addition

$$\left.\begin{aligned} \sum_1 x_{1i} &= 590, \\ \sum_2 x_{2i} &= 1144. \end{aligned}\right\} \tag{10.20}$$

Then

$$\left(\sum_1 x_{1i}\right)^2 \Big/ n_1 = 590^2/10 = 34\,810,$$

$$\left(\sum_2 x_{2i}\right)^2 \Big/ n_2 = 1144^2/22 = 59\,488.$$

From (9.11)

$$\sum_1 (x_{1i} - \bar{x}_1)^2 = 67^2 + 79^2 + \ldots + 60^2 - 34\,810$$

$$= 35\,532 - 34\,810$$

$$= 722, \tag{10.21}$$

$$\sum_2 (x_{2i} - \bar{x}_2)^2 = 64^2 + 41^2 + \ldots + 40^2 - 59\,488$$

$$= 62\,298 - 59\,488$$

$$= 2810. \tag{10.22}$$

Hence from (10.13)

$$s^2 = \frac{722 + 2810}{9 + 21}$$

$$= \frac{3532}{30}$$

$$= 117 \cdot 7. \tag{10.24}$$

5

The stage is now set for the final steps of calculation. From (8.5), (10.17), (10.20), and (10.24),

$$X = 52\cdot 0 - 59\cdot 0 = -7\cdot 0, \tag{8.11}$$

$$s_X^2 = 117\cdot 7(\tfrac{1}{10} + \tfrac{1}{22}) = 17\cdot 12 = (4\cdot 14)^2. \tag{10.25}$$

Therefore, for testing the null hypothesis of no difference between the two distributions

$$t = \frac{-7\cdot 0}{4\cdot 14}$$

$$= -1\cdot 69 \text{ with 30 d.f.} \tag{10.26}$$

Table 9.2 does not show entries for 30 d.f., but for a double-tail probability 0·05 the tabular value clearly would lie between 2·08 and 2·02. Thus the deviation of $|t|$ from zero is not statistically significant, and on the evidence available the null hypothesis that treatments A, D have the same distribution of rates of oxygen uptake is not to be rejected. The quantity 4·14 is the S.E. of X (section 10.4), and the observed difference in means may be written $-7\cdot 0 \pm 4\cdot 14$.

Reference to a more complete table shows 2·042 as the 0·05 probability level of t with 30 d.f. Hence the more general null hypothesis involving different means can be used, much as in section 8.5, to give the statement

$$-7\cdot 0 - 2\cdot 042 \times 4\cdot 14 \leqslant \xi_2 - \xi_1 \leqslant -7\cdot 0 + 2\cdot 042 \times 4\cdot 14$$

or

$$-15\cdot 5 \leqslant \xi_2 - \xi_1 \leqslant 1\cdot 5. \tag{10.27}$$

The fiducial limits to the difference between means, calculated (at probability 0·95) entirely from the evidence of the data, are $-15\cdot 5$ and 1·5. This last calculation corresponds very closely with that at the end of section 10.2.

10.8   STATISTICAL PRACTICE

In previous chapters, methods of statistical analysis and numerical examples have been used to illustrate the statistical thought that is relevant to the examination of treatment means in experiments such as Experiment ONE, TWO, and THREE. Although the examples presented in sections 6.6, 6.8, 8.4, and 8.5 are perfectly valid in the circumstances described, real experimental situations seldom correspond exactly with these. In order to concentrate attention on the most important concepts relating to frequency distributions, significance tests, fiducial limits, and associated probabilistic ideas, the variance per observation was supposed numerically known to the investigator, a most unusual state of affairs.

Now in section 10.1, 10.2, 10.6, 10.7 methods have been described and numerically illustrated that correspond exactly with standard statistical practice. Hypothetical 'data' have still been employed for the sake of arithmetical simplicity, but the pattern of computation and all the statistical logic are completely those used regularly by the applied statistician.

The reader should note that the methods do not require any knowledge of variability external to the evidence provided by the observation; they lead to conclusions based solely on these observations and the general theory of the t distribution. The method for comparing two means (sections 10.6, 10.7) is of especially great practical importance. These methods are among the more elementary used by the applied statistician, but they have many features in common with the more complicated ones (cf. section 11.12).

*10.9   VARIANCE RATIO DISTRIBUTION

Another important standard distribution can be derived from the Normal distribution. Little will be said about it here, and none of the theory will be presented, but it must be mentioned both because of the link it provides between other distributions and because of its many applications.

Suppose that s_1^2, s_2^2 are estimators of σ^2, which follow the distribution (9.32) with degrees of freedom f_1, f_2 respectively and which are independently distributed. Write

$$F = s_1^2/s_2^2. \tag{10.28}$$

By methods analogous to those of section 9.10, the distribution of F can be found. The distribution of s_1^2, s_2^2 jointly is written down as the product of two expressions like (9.32), then (10.28) is used so as to introduce F as a variate in place of s_1^2, and the resulting joint distribution of s_2^2, F is integrated with respect to s_2^2 over the range $(0, \infty)$.

The result obtained for the p.d.f. of F is

$$f(F) = \text{constant} \times F^{(f_1-2)/2}(f_2+f_1 F)^{-(f_1+f_2)/2}, \tag{10.29}$$

where F takes values in the range $(0, \infty)$. This can be used in examination of the null hypothesis expressed by

$$E(s_1^2) = E(s_2^2). \tag{10.30}$$

If observations are made and a particular pair of values of s_1^2, s_2^2 calculated, then a value of F differing greatly from unity will suggest that the null hypothesis is false; F will tend to be greater than or less than unity according as $E(s_1^2)$ or $E(s_2^2)$ is the larger. A test of significance can be based upon the integral

$$\int_F^\infty u^{(f_1-2)/2}(f_2+f_1 u)^{-(f_1+f_2)/2}\,du. \tag{10.31}$$

The constant required for the honesty condition has been omitted. This again corresponds to a standard type of integral, the Beta function, which is allied to the Γ function (section 9.4). The pair of degrees of freedom, f_1 and f_2, is required for its exact specification. Tables have been prepared to show the value of F that makes the integral take a specified value (such as $0 \cdot 1$, $0 \cdot 05$, $0 \cdot 01$), for different pairs of (f_1, f_2).

This is known as the *variance ratio distribution* or the *F distribution*. Sometimes the tabulation is given in terms of z, where

$$z = \tfrac{1}{2}\log_e F; \tag{10.32}$$

the z distribution has advantages for interpolation and is also of historic interest.

*10.10　Inter-relation of Distributions

Heuristic argument suggests the following relations:

F with f_1, f_2 degrees of freedom has the same distribution as $1/F$ with f_2, f_1 degrees of freedom;

F with $1, f_2$ degrees of freedom has the same distribution as t^2 with f_2 degrees of freedom;

F with f_1, ∞ degrees of freedom has the same distribution as s^2/σ^2 or χ^2/f_1 with f_1 degrees of freedom;

F with 1, ∞ degrees of freedom has the same distribution as the square of a variate distributed $N(0, 1)$.

Study of the form of the F distribution and of appropriate limits shows the truth of all these. Hence the F distribution is in a sense a generalisation of all these important distributions of continuous variates.

*10.11　Analysis of Variance

One of the most used techniques of statistical science is that known as *analysis of variance*. Though not intrinsically difficult, any adequate account of it falls outside the present scope. Equation (10.10) is a simple example: on the right-hand side of this equation, the first two terms relate to variation within treatment groups and the third term relates to the difference between treatments. If an analogous experiment had v treatments instead of only two, the first two terms generalise into v terms for variation within treatment groups; the next term, a generalised measure of differences between means for treatments, can also be put into the form of a sum of squares of deviations. On the null hypothesis that all treatments are alike in effect, an estimate of the error variance, σ^2, can be derived from each component and the two estimates are statistically independent; any true difference between treatment means will not affect the mean square within treatments but will tend to increase that between treatments. The F distribution provides a test of significance based upon the ratio of the two estimates.

Experiments of more complicated design, such as those described in Chapter 11, give rise to more complicated analogues of equation (10.10), with many components. Each such experiment has a corresponding analysis of variance in which, under various relevant null hypotheses, different mean squares estimate the same σ^2. An example appears in section 11.12, but this is intended only to illustrate the appearance of a very important method and not to instruct in its use. Any statistician, or any scientist who uses statistical procedures, needs to acquire thorough familiarity with the analysis of variance; no more can be said here.

EXERCISES

10.1 On the assumption that the 6 observations used in section 9.9 are normally distributed, find fiducial limits for the population mean at probabilities 0·95 and 0·99. Discuss whether a belief that the population mean is 28 is tenable.

10.2 On the sports pages of a daily newspaper, count the number of words in the first sentence of each of several distinct items. Do the same for several items of political news. You will need to establish conventions for counting numerals and abbreviations: specify these carefully. Take at least 10 items in all, not less than 3 from either source, and preferably unequal numbers from the two sources. Assume the t distribution to be applicable, and with its aid report on the difference between 'mean lengths of first sentences' from the two sources.

10.3 The observations x, y both have expectations θ. They have independent probability distributions (not necessarily Normal), with variances σ_x^2, σ_y^2. Using Theorem III, write down the expectation and variance of $(ax+by)/(a+b)$, where a, b are arbitrary numerical values. Determine the ratio $a:b$ that minimises the variances. Extend this result to $(ax+by+cz)/(a+b+c)$, where z is an observation with expectation θ, variance σ_z^2 and c is also arbitrary, the ratios $a:b:c$ now requiring determination.

10.4 Police records for a certain town show 100 convictions of motorists for offences against traffic regulations in January to March 1966, 200 in July to September 1966; the numbers of women offenders were 8 and 28 respectively in the two periods. Make a null hypothesis that the population proportion of women among all offenders is the same in both periods and estimate this as $(8+28)/(100+200)$. Hence estimate the variances for the observed proportions of women in the two periods, by equations (4.36), (8.4), and so (Theorems III, IV) estimate the variance of the difference between the observed proportions. Assuming Theorem VI to be applicable, test the statistical significance of the difference.

Suppose the figures for the two periods had been 32 out of 400 and 112 out of 800 (i.e. exactly 4 times as great); again test the null hypothesis.

Discuss critically the use of such evidence and tests in an enquiry into the proposition that women are (relative to men) more careless about compliance with traffic regulations in summer than in winter. Do not restrict consideration to mathematical theory, but take account also of the nature of the data!

10.5 With reference to the following situation, explain carefully the terms *null hypothesis*, *test of statistical significance*, *standard error*, *degrees of freedom*, and *estimation*.

A shoe manufacturer wishes to compare two types of sole leather. He chooses 10 men from his staff; to each of 5 of these, chosen at random, he presents a pair of shoes soled with leather A, and to each of the remaining five he presents a pair of shoes of identical style soled with leather Z. Each pair is inspected weekly, and a record is made of the number of days on which the shoes were actually worn; they are judged to require repair for the first time after the following numbers of days:

Leather A: 120, 110, 150, 80, 90,

Leather Z: 100, 30, 60, 90, 120.

Estimate the mean difference in 'life' of the two types of sole and its standard error. State clearly the conclusions to be drawn from the analysis with the aid of a significance test. [For a double-tailed probability of 0·05, and 8, 9, 10, 11 d.f., the value of t is 2·31, 2·26, 2·23, 2·20 respectively.]

10.6 Under the conditions of section 10.9, and with the aid of (10.30), (10.31), show that the probability that an observed F exceeds a specified F_0 is

$$(1+F_0)^{-1} \quad \text{for } f_1 = 2, f_2 = 2,$$
$$(1+\tfrac{1}{2}F_0)^{-2} \quad \text{for } f_1 = 2, f_2 = 4.$$

Generalise these results for $f_1 = 2, f_2 =$ any even integer.

10.7 Use Exercise 10.6 to construct a table of the value of F_P, the value of F that will be exceeded with probability P, for all combinations of $f_1 = 2; f_2 = 2, 4, 6, 8; P = 0·5, 0·1, 0·05, 0·01$.

Chapter 11

DESIGN OF EXPERIMENTS

11.1 PURPOSE OF DESIGN

When the treatments to be included in an experiment have been determined, the investigator will wish to compare them as precisely as possible. This may be interpreted as minimising the range of estimation expressed by fiducial limits or as maximising the chance of classifying differences as significant when in reality the corresponding null hypotheses are untrue. These and other criteria effectively reduce to minimisation of standard errors or variances of differences between means.

In earlier chapters, discussion has been restricted almost completely to experiments with two treatments. Scientific and technological investigations often require that three or more treatments be compared simultaneously. Most commonly, all treatments are of equal interest. An ideal experiment would therefore have the same variance for every treatment mean (of the form σ^2/n for appropriate n) or, rather more to the point, the variance of the difference between a pair of treatment means would be the same for every pair ($2\sigma^2/n$). Intuition and theory indicate that a considerable symmetry is desirable and that usually equal replication of all treatments will be wanted—that is to say, equal numbers of animals, or other experimental units, for each treatment. There are many circumstances in which special conditions inhibit the introduction of complete symmetry but almost inevitably raise questions of partial symmetry. However, study of these requires first an understanding of the simple symmetrical designs, and little beyond that will be possible here. This introduces many problems of combinatorial analysis and related topics.

A range of experimental situations will be discussed here, and proposals made for suitable designs. Thus the most important classes of design will be illustrated and some of their combinatorial problems

124

mentioned. Although not explicitly mentioned every time, it is to be understood that all designs require randomisation before use.

11.2 RANDOMISED BLOCKS

The pairing of animals of common parentage that has been used as part of the structure of Experiment TWO in earlier discussions (sections 6.6, 10.2) contains the seed of more complex designs. Its merit is the utilisation of a likelihood that two closely related animals will be more similar in a measurable characteristic than two unrelated animals. Although described in terms of a close blood-relationship between members of a pair, this is not an essential feature of the pairing procedure. Any other system of classifying 32 rats into 16 pairs could be made the basis of a change from Experiment THREE to Experiment TWO; for example, rats might be paired on account of likeness of coat colour, or approximately equal weight, or similar performance in threading a maze. Always the main consideration should be whether, in respect of the measurement under study, the members of a pair are likely to be similar except for the effects of any imposed treatments; sometimes in addition the pairing contributes to the convenience of the investigator in conducting the experiment.

When more than two treatments must be compared simultaneously, an obvious generalisation of pairing is available. The animals are grouped with the aid of any character thought relevant (blood-relationship, similarity of recent environment, similarity of size or colour, etc.), so that each group or *block* contains as many animals as there are treatments. If a larger stock of animals is available but the number to be used in the experiment is predetermined, the appropriate number of blocks of the right size is formed so as to make each block as internally homogeneous as is practicable. The animals of the first block are identified by numbers or otherwise, and one chosen at random for each treatment; with a new randomisation each time, every block is divided so as to give one animal for each treatment. This is known as a *randomised block* design. Of course, the same principles apply when the experimental unit is not an animal; it may be a tree, a transistor, a sheet of metal, a bacterial culture, an area of land on which barley is to be grown, or a man. As a short word for all types of experimental unit, *plot* is commonly used, so betraying the origin of many of these ideas in agricultural research.

Sometimes the material on which the experiment is to be conducted is already classified into an obviously suitable system of blocks, as when several litters of animals are to be used and the number of animals in each litter is equal to the number of treatments. Sometimes two or more possible systems of blocks exist. The investigator must either look for a more sophisticated design (section 11.3) or use whatever knowledge he has in order to guess which system will make his blocks the more homogeneous within themselves in respect of the measurement he proposes to study: are boxes of eggs from different flocks of hens at the same season likely to be more alike (in respect of some quality assessment) than boxes from the same flock at different seasons, before the imposition of treatment differences such as alternative methods of handling and storage? Sometimes the natural block size (number of plots per block) differs from the number of treatments, and other special steps may be taken (sections 11.6, 11.7). Sometimes there is no obvious system of blocking, yet the investigator may still choose to group together plots or units by taking account of some property that may be related to the ultimate measurement; for example, in comparing the yields of several varieties of a crop plant, the propinquity of plots of land in a field is often made the basis of a system of blocks. Such a procedure may give no gains but is unlikely to be disadvantageous.

The randomised block design is exceedingly flexible, being applicable to any number of blocks and treatments. For example, if A, B, C, D, E, F, G indicate 7 treatments and the experimenter proposes to try each on 5 different experimental units, he would take 35 plots grouped into 5 blocks of 7, making each set of 7 as homogeneous as he could. He would then take the 7 plots of Block I in any convenient order and assign the letters A, B, ..., G to them strictly at random. He would repeat for Blocks II, III, IV, V using an independent random allocation each time. Table 11.1 illustrates a possibility.

TABLE 11.1

Illustration of a randomised block design

Plot no.

Block	1	2	3	4	5	6	7
I	B	E	G	F	D	A	C
II	F	G	E	C	D	A	B
III	A	B	D	F	C	G	E
IV	C	G	E	D	A	B	F
V	D	C	B	A	G	F	E

Experiment ONE might be conducted in 8 blocks of 4 plots, perhaps using each litter to supply one block of 4 male rats and a second block of 4 females.

Rather rarely in experimental practice, a situation is encountered in which no basis for blocking can be proposed (cf. Experiment THREE). The number of plots to be allocated to each treatment will then be decided (usually the same number for every treatment), and these will be chosen completely at random from all available. This constitutes a *completely randomised* design or a design with *unrestricted randomisation*.

11.3 LATIN SQUARES

The randomised block principle involves one constraint of design, the representation of every treatment in every block. Sometimes an experimenter will wish to use two constraints simultaneously. For example, if for Experiment ONE the animals within a litter differed widely in size, he might wish to ensure a balancing of treatments over size of animal as well as over litter. Alternatively, if four rats could be measured per day instead of two, an additional constraint could ensure that one rat from each litter was measured on each of eight days. The appropriate design for such a situation is based on *Latin squares*. A Latin square is defined as a configuration of k different letters, each repeated k times, and arranged in k rows and k columns so as to have each letter once in each row and once in each column. Table 11.2 illustrates a pair of 4×4 squares that might be used for Experiment ONE, using litters and relative weight within the litter as constraints (and for the present supposing the limitation of measuring only two rats per day to be unimportant).

TABLE 11.2

Illustration of a pair of Latin squares suitable for Experiment ONE

		Litter no.			
		I	II	III	IV
Females	Heaviest	C	D	A	B
	2nd heaviest	B	A	C	D
	3rd heaviest	D	C	B	A
	Lightest	A	B	D	C
Males	Heaviest	B	C	A	D
	2nd heaviest	D	A	C	B
	3rd heaviest	A	D	B	C
	Lightest	C	B	D	A

Latin squares can be constructed for any value of k, but they are appreciably less numerous than the corresponding randomised blocks.

It is easily verified that the number of possible arrangements in k randomised blocks of k plots is $(k!)^k$; no formula is known for the corresponding number of Latin squares, but they have been enumerated up to $k=7$. The following may be of interest:

k	No. of randomised blocks $(k!)^k$	No. of Latin squares
2	4	2
3	216	12
4	331, 776	576
5	24, 883, 200, 000	161, 280

For the experiment implied by Table 11.2, a random choice should be made of two squares from the 576 possible.

11.4 STATISTICAL ANALYSIS

The main principle of statistical analysis for these and more complex experiments is that of the analysis of variance (section 10.11). For the experiment in Table 11.2, for example, this enables the sum of squares of deviations of the measurements on the 32 animals to be partitioned into components for litters, and for sex and relative weight within litters (which are not of primary interest in discussion of effects of treatments), for treatments, and for residual error variation. The two last components are the most interesting. Each may be divided by an associated number of degrees of freedom to give a corresponding *mean square*. Table 11.16 illustrates this. The null hypothesis that the treatments are without differential effects may be proved to require that both mean squares have the same expectation, σ^2, and a test of significance can be based upon the extent to which their ratio departs from unity; as usual, this embodies an assumption of Normal error variation or a sufficient approximation to Normality for the central limit theorem to protect the inferences. The mean square from the final component is the estimate of variance per plot, from which standard errors of means can be calculated essentially as described in Chapter 10.

   It is not intended to give here any detailed discussion of the statistical analysis. What must be emphasised is that the pattern of analysis is determined by the family of designs from which random selection is made for an experiment. Any Latin square configuration could arise by chance as a particular allocation of treatments according to randomised blocks; if (and only if) it has been chosen from the more restricted set of Latin squares, it must be analysed as a Latin square design and not by the analogous procedure appropriate to randomised blocks. Similarly, a design chosen as one of a family of randomised blocks is not to be analysed as though it consisted of one or more Latin squares simply because the arrangement of treatment symbols happens to conform to Latin square constraints.

Section 11.12, which may be read at this point by those who wish, presents briefly a numerical example of calculations for an experiment corresponding to Table 11.2. No attempt is made to explain the theory. Some may like to search for analogies with methods of Chapter 10; these exist, but are by no means obvious.

*11.5 Graeco-Latin Squares

A $k \times k$ Latin square can be thought of as a specification of k^2 conjunctions of one of k 'rows' with one of k 'columns' and simultaneously with one of k 'letters', such that every possible pair of row and column, of row and letter, and of column and letter occurs once. The idea can be extended by having k Greek letters as well as k Latin letters, and seeking k^2 conjunctions of one from each of the four categories such that all possible pairings of each of six kinds appear. Table 11.3 shows one way of doing this by adding Greek letters to the second square in Table 11.2.

Table 11.3

Illustration of a Graeco-Latin square

$B\delta$	$C\beta$	$A\alpha$	$D\gamma$
$D\alpha$	$A\gamma$	$C\delta$	$B\beta$
$A\beta$	$D\delta$	$B\gamma$	$C\alpha$
$C\gamma$	$B\alpha$	$D\beta$	$A\delta$

An arrangement of this kind, known as a *Graeco-Latin square*, may be useful for incorporation of further constraints, but its greater importance lies in other types of design that can be constructed with its aid. Graeco-Latin squares have considerable intrinsic interest for the mathematician. Rather few Latin squares can be augmented by k Greek letters in the manner of Table 11.3. Indeed, for the other square in Table 11.2, this is impossible, as trial rapidly shows. For $k=2$ and $k=6$, no Graeco-Latin squares exist; for all other k, some can be found though they are much scarcer than the simple Latin squares. (Proofs for the previous sentence are difficult!) This statement includes an interesting topic in the history of mathematics. As long ago as 1782, Euler speculated that no Graeco-Latin square could be constructed if k were an even number not divisible by 4; proof was elusive, but the speculation was widely believed until in 1959 it was disproved by demonstration of how to construct squares for $k = 10$, 14, etc. The square in Table 11.3 can easily be further augmented by use of another set of k symbols, say Gothic letters, in a balanced manner, so creating a more complicated type of *orthogonal square*.

11.6 DESIGNING A MODIFIED EXPERIMENT ONE

Now that some ideas on experiments for the simultaneous comparison of several treatments have been developed, suggestions can be made for the design of Experiment ONE under the conditions described in section 2.1. Each of the four litters of rats available for use includes four males and four females. If there is any fear of inherent differences between litters or between sexes in their average rates for oxygen uptake by red blood cells, the physiologist will be wise to ensure that each of the four treatments is allotted to one male and one female in each litter. Even if he has no prior belief that such differences will occur, insurance against the risk is easy and cannot do any harm. Any other arrangement is bound to give unequal representation of litters or of sexes in the treatments, and consequently differences between mean rates calculated for the four treatments would be subject to disturbance by inherent litter or sex differences.

A randomised block design with each of its eight blocks containing four litter mates of like sex would achieve this much: in each block, one rat would be chosen at random for each treatment. This takes no account of constraints on the physiologist's time. The reader may not have noticed that in discussions of Experiments TWO and THREE in sections 6.6, 8.1, and elsewhere nothing has been said about one important condition: section 2.1 stated that only two rats per day could be measured, and sections 2.4, 2.5 implied that this also applied to Experiments TWO and THREE.

If the measurement of oxygen uptake is in any way affected by subjective influences, values obtained on different days may differ consistently quite independently of true differences in the animals: the state of health of the physiologist or his assistants could affect the measurements to an extent that is doubtless small but perhaps neither negligible nor predictable. In Experiment TWO (section 6.6), the natural procedure would be to arrange that each pair of litter mates is measured on the same day. Just as the experimental design and the statistical analysis described in section 6.6 eliminated differences between litters, so they will simultaneously eliminate differences between days of measurement. In Experiment THREE (section 8.4), the design cannot be adapted so as to accommodate a balancing over days of measurement because of the unequal numbers of subjects; if important day-to-day differences were suspected, more complicated computing procedures would be needed. However, if the recommendation of section 8.6 is accepted, the numbers of subjects on the two treatments would be made equal, and the experiment could then be conducted by assigning one randomly selected rat from each treatment to each of 16 measurement days. Such a procedure immediately establishes a pairing of the rats essentially similar to that of Experiment TWO, and the statistical analysis of sections 6.6, 6.8, 10.2 becomes appropriate.

Experiment ONE cannot be arranged in this fashion, because the number of treatments exceeds the number of measurements possible per day. For the discussion in this section, a relaxation of conditions will be assumed: the determinations to be made on each rat will be supposed such that four animals can be measured each day, instead of only two. The design in eight randomised blocks described above could then be adapted in the way proposed for Experiment TWO. On each of eight measurement days, one of the eight blocks would be selected at random and all the four rats in it measured. The arrangement in Table 11.4 is an example of what might be done. Note that no differentiation is made between the animals in a block on account of any individual characteristics such as weight (cf. Table 11.2); random allocation to A, B, C, D is implied.

TABLE 11.4

First suggested design for a modified Experiment ONE
(Arabic numerals denote eight measurement days)

	Male rats				Female rats			
	A	B	C	D	A	B	C	D
Litter I	7	7	7	7	5	5	5	5
Litter II	4	4	4	4	2	2	2	2
Litter III	1	1	1	1	6	6	6	6
Litter IV	8	8	8	8	3	3	3	3

Although the design in Table 11.4 is adequate for estimating differences between rates of oxygen uptake in either sex or averaged over both sexes, it is far from satisfactory for estimating the simple difference between males and females. This sex difference can be estimated only as a comparison between measurements on different days. Both the sex difference and average differences between litters are said to be *confounded* with mean differences between days of measurement, in that any numerical value of one is necessarily also a numerical value for the other kind of difference. This is in the sense that the average difference between the sexes is simultaneously the average difference between days 1, 4, 7, 8 and days 2, 3, 5, 6. Similarly, the average difference between two litters is simultaneously a difference between two pairs of days.

Table 11.5 indicates one way of overcoming the weakness. The two blocks (days) for one litter are rearranged so that each includes two rats of each sex, while still maintaining the condition that each treatment appears once on each day. Consequently, average differences between treatments are as well estimated as before, being free of any distortion from average differences between days or between sexes. The average difference between sexes is now balanced over days, each sex being used twice per day. Necessarily something is sacrificed, and in fact if the investigator wishes to look at treatment effects in males (or in females) alone he will find the new design less satisfactory than that in Table 11.4. Once again, random allocation of animals to treatments is implied except in so far as Table 11.5 restricts it.

TABLE 11.5

Second suggested design for a modified Experiment ONE

	Male rats				Female rats			
	A	B	C	D	A	B	C	D
Litter I	7	7	5	5	5	5	7	7
Litter II	4	2	4	2	2	4	2	4
Litter III	1	6	6	1	6	1	1	6
Litter IV	8	8	3	3	3	3	8	8

Note that this design would gain in symmetry if six litters were available. Each of the possible ways of dividing four objects into two pairs could then be the structural basis of two blocks; as things are, one division is used twice and the other two once. The exact sense in which information is lost cannot be explained here; inspection of Table 11.5 indicates that an attempt to discover whether the difference between A and B is greater in males than in females would be balanced in respect of measurement days for days 3, 5, 7, 8 but would involve any average difference between days 2 and 4 or between days 1 and 6.

In section 2.1, information on differences between litters and on any time trend was said to be useful. The designs in Tables 11.4, 11.5 are poor for this purpose, because both confound litter differences with differences between days of measurement: in both designs, the difference between litters I and III is estimated by the same quantity that estimates the average difference between days 5, 7 and days 1, 6. Table 11.6 shows how Latin squares can be used to remove this weakness. The difference between any pair of days is now balanced in respect of litters, but the sex difference is still confounded with days.

TABLE 11.6

Third suggested design for a modified Experiment ONE

	Male rats				Female rats			
	A	B	C	D	A	B	C	D
Litter I	5	1	7	3	8	4	2	6
Litter II	3	7	1	5	4	8	6	2
Litter III	1	5	3	7	2	6	4	8
Litter IV	7	3	5	1	6	2	8	4

A combination of the ideas underlying Tables 11.5, 11.6 produces perhaps the best type of design for this experiment. This (Table 11.7) retains the balance of litters over days, has each treatment on one animal of each sex from each litter and also each treatment once on each day, and also has a balance for sex in respect of litters, of treatments, and of days. If differences between effects of treatments are equal for males and females, it should be satisfactory, but any attempt to examine whether

TABLE 11.7

Fourth suggested design for a modified Experiment ONE

	Male rats				Female rats			
	A	B	C	D	A	B	C	D
Litter I	5	1	7	3	6	2	8	4
Litter II	4	8	2	6	3	7	1	5
Litter III	1	5	3	7	2	6	4	8
Litter IV	8	4	6	2	7	3	5	1

the difference between A and D is greater for males than for females runs into trouble because of a confounding with days.

The merits of alternative designs have been discussed here only in very general terms. More objective assessment can be made by studying the statistical analysis appropriate to each and calculating from it factors by which σ^2, the variance per rat, would be multiplied in order to give variances for important comparisons. A very simple illustration of such a procedure was given in section 8.6; for present purposes, a compromise has to be sought between optimal requirements for several different types of comparison. Too few rats are available for all the aims listed in section 2.1 to be attained satisfactorily.

The designs in Tables 11.4–11.7 are shown here merely to illustrate the combinatorial complexities that may be employed in deciding how to conduct an experiment. Before any of them was used, the allocation of individual rats to treatments and days would be randomised, subject to the restrictions implicit in the design. The manner of doing this will not be described, as it depends upon a more exact specification of the combinatorial properties than has been deemed necessary, but essentially it requires that one allocation be chosen at random from all those that satisfy the restrictions. In fact, the investigator from Chapter 2 might be wise to abandon some of his declared interests; his number of rats is small for the study of the range of questions he is asking, and fuller examination of the statistical analyses appropriate to Tables 11.4–11.7 may show that the answers will necessarily be so inadequate that more modest aims ought to be adopted.

11.7   INCOMPLETE BLOCKS

Earlier sections of this chapter have been concerned with randomised block designs and developments from these. Each treatment was included once in each block. Desirable though this is, it is not always possible. Not infrequently, the number of plots available per block is less than the number of treatments: a variant of Experiment ONE might have had five treatments instead of four, still with need to accommodate these in blocks of four litter-mates. The need then is to devise a symmetrical pattern of omissions of treatments.

For example, assessment of flavour and other subjective characteristics of foodstuffs is often based upon ratings given by panels of judges (either 'experts' or chosen to represent typical consumers). A judge asked to compare the flavours of different samples of fish, of tea, or of ice cream, and to assign marks to each, will be confused and will become unreliable if he is asked to deal with many samples at the same time. Probably 3 or 4 per judge is enough, yet a greater number of samples may need comparison. Table 11.8 shows an arrangement in which seven judges test seven sources of a food $(A, B, \ldots, G)$, in such a way that each judge receives only four and each source is tested by four judges.

TABLE 11.8

Design for a comparison of seven sources of food by seven judges

Judge I	C,	F,	G,	E
Judge II	G,	D,	F,	A
Judge III	A,	E,	B,	G
Judge IV	B,	A,	F,	C
Judge V	B,	C,	G,	D
Judge VI	D,	E,	A,	C
Judge VII	E,	D,	B,	F

The special feature of the design is that not only does each treatment occur the same number of times (here four), but each pair of treatments occurs with the same judge the same number of times (here two: B and G occur with judges III and V). This is known as a *balanced incomplete block design*, and its special symmetry ensures that all comparisons between pairs of treatments are estimated with equal variance. In general, if t treatments (do not confuse t with the use of this symbol in previous chapters!) are to be tested in b blocks with k units or plots per block, *necessary* conditions for the existence of a balanced incomplete block design are that r and λ shall both be integers, where

$$r = bk/t \qquad (11.1)$$

is the number of plots of each treatment and

$$\lambda = r(k-1)/(t-1) \qquad (11.2)$$

is the number of blocks in which each pair of treatments occurs. Table 11.8 refers to $t=b=7$, $k=r=4$, $\lambda=2$, but many designs exist with $t \neq b$; for example, there is a design with $t=21$, $b=30$, $k=7$, $r=10$, $\lambda=3$. The conditions are not *sufficient*: no design exists with $t=15$, $b=21$, $k=5$, $r=7$, $\lambda=2$, although these integers satisfy (11.1), (11.2).

Although many ways of constructing designs of this family are known, no general procedure (other than systematic exhaustive trial) for discovering whether designs for a set of parameters satisfying (11.1), (11.2) exist and enumerating them has been found. The subject is analogous to that of Latin and Graeco-Latin squares in its difficulties. Some additional necessary conditions are known. One is that $t \leqslant b$; another is that if $t = b =$ an even number, then $r(t-k)/(t-1)$ must be a perfect square.

Table 11.8 could be used with randomisation of order within each block. However, if each judge is expected to finish with one sample before starting another (instead of, for example, having four cups of tea in front of him and sipping as he wishes until he decides how many marks to give each), the order may be important. The palate may become jaded after two or three samples and be less sensitive to delicate flavours for the fourth. Table 11.9 shows how a constraint can be put upon order of presentation to the judges so that each source of food occupies the first, second, third, and fourth position once. Such a *Youden square* can always be constructed if b/t is an integer.

TABLE 11.9

The design of Table 11.8 with balance of order

	Judge						
	I	II	III	IV	V	VI	VII
First sample	C	A	B	F	G	E	D
Second sample	F	G	A	B	C	D	E
Third sample	G	D	E	A	B	C	F
Fourth sample	E	F	G	C	D	A	B

In taste testing of this kind, there is the possibility that a judge will tend to mark one of the samples submitted to him particularly highly if others in the same block are much poorer. If such an inter-relation of scores is to be studied, a further desirable constraint is that every possible set of three treatments shall occur together in a block the same number of times. A necessary condition then is that

$$\lambda' = \lambda(k-2)/(t-2) \qquad (11.3)$$

shall be an integer. Non-trivial designs with this double balance are scarce; one exists for $t = 10$, $b = 30$, $k = 4$, $r = 12$, but a more thorough search and study is needed.

Relaxation of the restriction (11.2) so as to permit different degrees of block association for different pairs of treatments produces a wider class of *partially balanced incomplete blocks*. This destroys the equality of variances for all comparisons between two treatments, an important consequence of the symmetry established by (11.2), but many designs are known that keep the inequalities of variance to a very low level.

11.8 Designing Experiment One

To meet the requirements of Experiment ONE by requiring measurement on only two rats per day can be seen to be much more difficult than to plan for four rats per day as in section 11.6. If day-to-day variation is likely to follow a fairly regular pattern, perhaps as a result of increasing technical skill of an operator or slow deterioration of a piece of apparatus on account of wear, one possibility would be to group together pairs of successive days and design so as to balance only over the four rats measured in a pair of days. The designs in section 11.6, and notably that in Table 11.7, remain applicable. If day-to-day variation depends upon uncontrolled air temperature in the laboratory, or haphazard changes in a component of the apparatus that must be renewed each day, or the state of the temper of the physiologist, this procedure may be almost useless.

Table 11.10 shows a modification of Table 11.4, in which each set of four like-sexed litter-mates is split between two days. For litters I and IV the split separates A, B from C, D in both sexes, for litter II, A, C and B, D are paired, and for litter III A, D and B, C. Note that the six pairs constitute a balanced incomplete block arrangement with $t=4$, $b=6$, $k=2$, but in Table 11.10 the balance is spoiled because two pairs must be used twice. Once again (cf. Table 11.5), six litters would permit a symmetry not achievable in four. The design in Table 11.10 has all the weaknesses of Table 11.4, and inevitably additional ones in that now differences between treatments are to some extent identical with differences between days: treatment differences are *partially confounded* with days.

The study of the average difference between sexes will be aided, again

TABLE 11.10

First suggested design for Experiment ONE

	Male rats				Female rats			
	A	B	C	D	A	B	C	D
Litter I	7	7	13	13	5	5	9	9
Litter II	4	16	4	16	2	8	2	8
Litter III	14	10	10	14	11	1	1	11
Litter IV	15	15	12	12	6	6	3	3

at some cost to the comparison of treatment differences in males and females, by the same sort of interchange (Table 11.11) that gave Table 11.5 from Table 11.4. Whether anything satisfactory can be done to distinguish day and litter differences without seriously reducing the value of the design for its main purpose of treatment comparisons is questionable. Probably Tables 11.10 and 11.11 represent about the best types of arrangement possible for an experimental situation that is really too complex for the number of animals available.

TABLE 11.11

Second suggested design for Experiment ONE

	Male rats				Female rats			
	A	B	C	D	A	B	C	D
Litter I	7	5	13	9	5	7	9	13
Litter II	4	16	2	8	2	8	4	16
Litter III	14	10	1	11	11	1	10	14
Litter IV	15	6	12	3	6	15	3	12

*11.9   RESIDUALS OF TREATMENTS

In some experiments where treatments are applied in sequence to the same subject, there is a possibility that the measurement associated with a particular 'plot' of a treatment may be affected by the treatment that the subject received immediately previously. For example, in the situation described before presentation of Table 11.9, a judge's marking of a sample of food from source B may be affected not only by intrinsic properties of B but also by whether the previous sample was good or poor. Various designs can be proposed that balance each treatment over alternative previous treatments and so allow residual influences of treatments to be estimated independently of direct effects. Table 11.12 shows such a design for food samples from four sources tested by 12 subjects; at the stage of the second sample, each letter follows each *other* letter once (for the second sample, C follows A for judge II, B for judge VIII, D for judge X, and similarly for other letters and later samples). Alternative rations for animal feeding may be similarly compared in their direct effects and in their residuals for a subsequent feeding period, the 'judges' now being test animals whose weight gains or milk productions are to be recorded.

A related class of designs is one for experiments in which one subject receives a long sequence of treatments. Table 11.13 shows examples of serially balanced sequences for 2, 3, 4, 5 treatments such that each letter in a sequence follows each other letter just once and, except for the initial letter, the sequence consists of successive blocks in which every treatment is represented. In the third example, the first B follows A, the second

TABLE 11.12

A design for balancing residuals

	Order of sample			
	First	Second	Third	Fourth
Judge I	B	D	A	C
Judge II	A	C	B	D
Judge III	C	A	D	B
Judge IV	D	B	C	A
Judge V	C	B	A	D
Judge VI	A	D	C	B
Judge VII	D	A	B	C
Judge VIII	B	C	D	A
Judge IX	A	B	D	C
Judge X	D	C	A	B
Judge XI	C	D	B	A
Judge XII	B	A	C	D

follows C, and the third B follows D. The reader should have no difficulty in inventing variations on these conditions so as to give different types of balance, but construction of arrangements to satisfy the conditions may be a difficult combinatorial problem.

TABLE 11.13

Examples of serially balanced sequence designs

$A \mid B, A$
$A \mid B, C, A \mid C, B, A$
$A \mid B, C, D, A \mid C, B, A, D \mid B, D, C, A$
$A \mid E, A, C, D, B \mid A, B, E, D, C \mid B, C, A, D, E \mid C, E, B, D, A$

11.10 FACTORIAL EXPERIMENTS

Some situations require that several *factors* be investigated in one experiment, and in others there are considerable gains to the breadth of inference from an experiment if two or more factors are included.

Experiment ONE could be termed a 4×2 factorial, in that it involved the four alternatives previously described as treatments in combination with the two sexes; interest lies in the treatment effects, in any average difference between males and females in rate of oxygen uptake, and in any *interaction* of effects such as the difference between two treatments being markedly greater for males than for females. Had the physiologist also wanted to study two alternative diets during the period between treatment and day of measurement, he would have needed a $4 \times 2 \times 2$ (or 4×2^2) factorial. He would then have hoped to try all combinations of treatment, sex, and diet. He could scarcely have done so adequately without a larger number of rats.

Experiments in which all factors are at the same number of *levels* (that just described is said to have one factor at 4 levels and two at 2 levels) are especially informative, adaptable, and interesting. The 2^p and 3^p (where p is the number of factors) series are particularly widely used. For example, an experiment in which animals are to be fed on one of two forms of protein with one of two forms of vitamin supplement and housed in one of two types of cage is a 2^3 factorial, and if each factor involved 3 possibilities instead of 2 it would be a 3^3. These experiments can be conducted in any design suitable for a total of 8 or 27 combinations of treatment, perhaps randomised blocks of 8 or some form of incomplete block design for 27 treatments. In no other way can investigation be made not only of the effect of change in form of protein or in vitamin supplement (on animal weight or whatever measurement is under study) but also of the extent to which either effect is modified by the state of the other factor (commonly termed the *interaction* of two factors), as well as of similar consequences of cage size and its interactions with the first two factors.

If p is at all large, the number of combinations of levels can be far too great for accommodation in simpler designs such as randomised blocks and Latin squares: an investigator may easily think of 5 or 6 factors, and $2^6 = 64$, $3^5 = 243$. The notion of confounding mentioned earlier (section 11.6) can be used to permit use of smaller incomplete blocks, in such a way that block differences are confounded with relatively uninteresting aspects of treatment comparisons (e.g. interactions of three or more factors simultaneously). Experiments can be conducted using only one plot of each combination of levels (243 plots for a 3^5 design) or even a fraction of this number (81 plots for a 3^5 design), if p is large; this requires special procedures for estimating σ^2. Theories of finite algebraic groups, of Galois fields, and of finite geometries help in the construction and understanding of these designs.

'Mixed' factorial designs, such as $3 \times 3 \times 2$ or $4 \times 3 \times 2$, are also important, but are more complicated and less adaptable.

11.11 AN APOLOGY

This chapter has attempted to give a rapid and highly condensed introduction to the theory and practice of experimental design. The student to whom the subject is entirely new must not expect to understand all the implications, or even to see immediately how each design has been constructed. He should try to follow the main combinatorial features, and should use the exercises at the end of the chapter to test his understanding of these; some are difficult!

More difficult than the construction of designs to meet stated combinatorial specifications is the choice of a design for use in a particular experimental situation. Study of the pattern of statistical analysis for alternative choices (cf. sections 11.4, 11.12) enables the variances of different comparisons of treatment means to be expressed as multiples of σ^2, the variance per plot. In all but the simplest cases, however, only a combination of knowledge of the aims of the experiment with statistical expertise can guide the decision on which set of multiples is optimal: seldom will one design show minimum variance for every interesting comparison, so that a compromise based on a balancing of gains and losses is usually needed. Sometimes the experienced statistician may suggest that a slight modification in the aims of the experiment, or in the resources made available, will permit a far better design to be chosen; exclusion of a treatment, addition of a level for one factor, or use of an extra litter of mice may help.

Even major treatises on the design of experiments, of which many have been published, can scarcely deal comprehensively with all these considerations. For the novice, the important thing is to be made aware of their existence, so that he does not believe the statistician's contribution to experimentation to consist solely of solving combinatorial puzzles and performing calculations like those in section 11.12. This chapter aims at nothing more than presenting the relatively easily comprehended combinatorial problems against a broader background of the strategy of experimentation. At the end of it, the student should at least appreciate its inadequacy and his own inexperience.

*11.12 NUMERICAL EXAMPLE

Suppose that the experiment whose design was illustrated in Table 11.2 gave the results shown in Table 11.14. Very simple numerical values have been assumed as the 'data' from this hypothetical experiment, but they may be regarded as measures of rates of oxygen uptake in some suitable units. In Table 11.14, the sex and weight grouping is simply labelled 'rows' and the litters simply 'columns', a convenient general terminology. The first step in the statistical analysis is to form totals of observations according to row, column, and treatment; these are summarised in Table 11.15. Note the check that the grand total, 308, is formed in three ways.

TABLE 11.14

'Data' from a hypothetical experiment with the design in Table 11.2

Columns

	1	2	3	4
Rows				
1	C: 9	D: 5	A: 8	B: 20
2	B: 19	A: 10	C: 2	D: 3
3	D: 4	C: 5	B: 7	A: 14
4	A: 12	B: 2	D: 5	C: 7
5	B: 22	C: 11	A: 14	D: 11
6	D: 11	A: 9	C: 12	B: 14
7	A: 13	D: 7	B: 10	C: 8
8	C: 7	B: 8	D: 7	A: 12

TABLE 11.15

Totals from Table 11.14

Row	1	2	3	4	5	6	7	8	All
	42	34	30	26	58	46	38	34	308

Column	1	2	3	4	All
	97	57	65	89	308

Treatment	A	B	C	D	All
	92	102	61	53	308

The analysis of variance, the standard statistical procedure for examining data of this kind, involves forming a sum of squares of deviations for all the observations and partitioning it. This sum of squares is

$$9^2 + 5^2 + 8^2 + \ldots + 7^2 + 12^2 - \frac{308^2}{32}, \tag{11.5}$$

which of course has 31 d.f. The *adjustment for the mean*, $308^2/32$, is needed several times, and therefore a separate record of it is kept. It and the sum of squares of deviations

$$3704 \cdot 00 - 2964 \cdot 50 = 739 \cdot 50 \tag{11.6}$$

are entered in the column of Table 11.16 headed 'Sums of squares'.

Of this total, seven d.f. are ascribable to differences between the eight rows, and this component is formed from the row totals in Table 11.15 as

$$(42^2 + 34^2 + \ldots + 34^2) \div 4 - 2964 \cdot 50 = 3144 \cdot 00 - 2964 \cdot 50$$

$$= 179 \cdot 50. \tag{11.7}$$

Here the divisor, 4, is the number of single observations contained in each of the totals whose squares are summed (42 is the sum of one entry from each of the four columns), and the adjustment for the mean appears again. The number of d.f. is one less than the number of totals (rows) used in the calculation.

Similarly three d.f. are ascribable to differences between columns, the component being

$$(97^2 + 57^2 + 65^2 + 89^2) \div 8 - 2964 \cdot 50 = 136 \cdot 00. \tag{11.8}$$

Each total that is squared contains 8 single observations, so that the divisor is 8.

For treatments, exactly as for columns, the component is

$$(92^2 + 102^2 + 61^2 + 53^2) \div 8 - 2964 \cdot 50 = 210 \cdot 25, \tag{11.9}$$

again with three d.f. because there are four treatments.

An essential feature for the validity of these calculations is the balance of each category in respect of the other two: each row includes one observation from each column and one from each treatment, each column includes one from each row and two from each treatment; each treatment includes one from each row and two from each column. Rows, columns, treatments are said to be mutually *orthogonal*. This ensures that the residual when the three sums of squares are subtracted from the total sum of squares itself has the properties of being a sum of squares of deviations (with the residual number of d.f.), although some more complicated algebra is needed in order to demonstrate the fact (cf. equation (10.10)). Hence the d.f. and sums of squares entries in Table 11.16 are completed by subtraction. Mean squares are obtained by dividing each sum of squares by its d.f.

A natural, though perhaps not immediately obvious, generalisation of earlier mathematical models corresponding to observations is to assert that in this experiment each observation is Normally distributed about an expectation which in turn is a sum of independent row, column, and

TABLE 11.16

Analysis of variance for Table 11.14

Adjustment for mean		2964·50	
Source of variation	d.f.	Sums of squares	Mean squares
Rows	7	179·50	25·64
Columns	3	136·00	45·33
Treatments	3	210·25	70·08
Residual (error)	18	213·75	11·88
Total	31	739·50	

treatment components (A84–A86). Under these conditions, one can prove that the expectation of the residual mean square is σ^2, the error variance per observation (A87–A92). Moreover, on the null hypothesis that treatments are all alike in their effects, the mean square for treatments has the same expectation (and is necessarily inflated if the null hypothesis is false). The two mean squares are independently distributed according to (9.32). Therefore their ratio has the distribution (10.29), and a significance test of this ratio tests the truth of the null hypothesis. Here

$$F = \frac{70·08}{11·88} = 5·9. \qquad (11.10)$$

Tables of the integral based on (10.29) show that the probability of a value of F at least as large as this is less than 0·01, so that by the usual argument the null hypothesis would be rejected.

Moreover, since

$$s^2 = 11·88 \qquad (11.11)$$

is an estimate of σ^2 with 18 d.f., the S.E. of each treatment mean in Table 11.17 is obtainable as

$$\sqrt{(s^2/8)} = 1·22. \qquad (11.12)$$

This can be used in tests of significance of differences between pairs of means in Table 11.17; note that the d.f. for t would be 18 (section 10.5). Very evidently, each of A, B differs from each of C, D, but the difference within each pair is within the limits of natural variability.

TABLE 11.17

Summary of treatment means from Table 11.14

A	B	C	D	
11·50	12·75	7·62	6·62	S.E.: $\pm 1·22$

Rows and columns can be examined similarly, but they are of lesser intrinsic interest. The function of these two classifications is to eliminate sources of variation, and this they have fulfilled, for had either or both of these constraints not been used the residual mean square would have been substantially larger.

Similar methods of analysis are applicable to designs such as those of Tables 11.1, 11.3, but the later designs of this chapter introduce additional complications.

EXERCISES

11.1 Prove (11.1), (11.2), (11.3). The first is almost obvious, the other two follow easily from the definitions.

11.2 List all the different 4×4 Latin squares in which *both* the first row *and* the first column are in the order $ABCD$. You will need to make a systematic and exhaustive enumeration. The Latin square property is not affected by applying any of the following procedures to any Latin square: (i) make any interchange of order of whole rows; (ii) make any interchange of order of whole columns; (iii) make any interchange of names between the letters. Hence show that the total number of different 4×4 Latin squares using letters A, B, C, D is the answer to the first part of the question multiplied by 4!3!

11.3 'Sixteen passengers on a liner discover that they are an exceptionally representative body. Four are Englishmen, four are Scots, four are Irish, and four are Welsh. There are also four each of four different ages, 35, 45, 55 and 65, and no two of the same age are of the same nationality. By profession also four are lawyers, four soldiers, four doctors and four clergymen, and no two of the same profession are of the same age or of the same nationality.

'It appears, also, that four are bachelors, four married, four widowed and four divorced, and that no two of the same marital status are of the same profession or the same age, or the same nationality. Finally, four are conservatives, four liberals, four socialists and four fascists, and no two of the same political sympathies are of the same marital status, or the same profession, or the same age, or the same nationality.

'Three of the fascists are known to be an unmarried English lawyer of 65, a married Scots soldier of 55 and a widowed Irish doctor of 45. It is then easy to specify the remaining fascist.

'It is further given that the Irish socialist is 35, the conservative of 45 is a Scotsman, and the Englishman of 55 is a clergyman. What do you know of the Welsh lawyer?'

[From *The Design of Experiments* by R. A. Fisher, the classical book on this subject.]

11.4 In the 4×4 Latin square

$$
\begin{array}{cccc}
\textcircled{A} & B & \textcircled{C} & D \\
B & \textcircled{A} & D & \textcircled{C} \\
C & \textcircled{D} & A & \textcircled{B} \\
\textcircled{D} & C & \textcircled{B} & A
\end{array}
$$

the letters encircled include two in each row, two in each column, and two of each of *A, B, C, D*. In how many different ways can this be done for this square, and for each of your squares in Exercise 11.2?

11.5 In the following 6×6 Latin square put circles around 18 of the 36 letters so as to satisfy the conditions that (i) three circles lie in each row; (ii) three circles lie in each column; (iii) the circles include each of *A, B, C, D, E, F* three times:

$$
\begin{array}{cccccc}
B & E & D & F & C & A \\
F & B & C & A & D & E \\
A & C & F & B & E & D \\
C & A & E & D & F & B \\
D & F & B & E & A & C \\
E & D & A & C & B & F
\end{array}
$$

[There are probably many completely different solutions.]

11.6 The Latin square

	Period			
	1	2	3	4
Animal I	B	D	C	A
Animal II	A	C	D	B
Animal III	C	B	A	D
Animal IV	D	A	B	C

is analogous to Table 11.12, without the restriction that *in each period* each letter should follow each other letter. Thus D follows B for animal I (period 2), C for II (period 3), and A for III (period 4).

Construct a 6×6 Latin square with balance of this kind.

This kind of balance cannot be achieved in *one* 5×5 Latin square, but it is possible to form *two* 5×5 Latin squares such that in all each letter follows each other letter twice. Can you construct an example?

11.7 Enumerate all possible sequences for four letters analogous to the third example in Table 11.13. Apart from permutations of letters, there are 14 different ones.

11.8 Analogous to Table 11.13 are sequences in which each letter follows every letter *including itself* once. For two letters:

$$A|A, B|B, A.$$

Show that no such sequences exist for three or four letters. (None exist for five letters, but there are sequences for six letters; proofs are more laborious!)

11.9 Show that a further square can be superposed on Table 11.3, using the symbols w, x, y, z such that

(i) the new symbols form a Latin square;
(ii) each of the 16 conjunctions of one of w, x, y, z with one of A, B, C, D occurs once;
(iii) each of the 16 conjunctions of one of w, x, y, z with one of $\alpha, \beta, \gamma, \delta$ occurs once.

[This is mentioned in the final sentence of section 11.5.]

11.10 Use Exercise 11.9 to construct a balanced incomplete block design with $t=16$, $b=20$, $k=4$, $r=5$, $\lambda=1$.

[Begin by writing the symbols for the 16 treatments, in any order, in 4 rows of 4.]

Chapter 12

THEORY OF ESTIMATION

12.1 Parameters and Statistics

A great part of the contents of earlier chapters has been concerned, directly or indirectly, with the examination of null hypotheses by significance tests and with estimating values for unknown parameters. It is now necessary to discuss the process of estimation more formally. This must include consideration of how observations are to be used in order to estimate a parameter, that is to say what function of them is to be calculated. In all the instances presented so far, the question of how to choose a suitable function has been evaded, and the obvious has been accepted almost without comment. In section 9.2, an 'obvious' estimator of variance was seen to require slight modification in order to meet reasonable requirements, but no general discussion was introduced.

A simple illustration indicates the danger of relying on the obvious. In (4.30), the mean of the distribution of a continuous variate whose p.d.f. is $f(x)$ was defined as

$$E(x) \equiv \mu = \int_{-\infty}^{\infty} x f(x) \, dx. \qquad (12.1)$$

If $x_1, x_2, \ldots, x_n$ is a random sample of n independent observations from this distribution, the obvious choice for an estimator of the parameter μ is the function well-known as the arithmetic mean of the sample:

$$\bar{x} = \sum_i x_i / n. \qquad (12.2)$$

Although this can never be said to be wrong (cf. section 12.4), distributions exist for which by any reasonable criteria $\bar{x}$ is rather a poor estimator for μ. For example, consider

$$
\begin{aligned}
f(x) &= \mu - x & \mu - 1 \leqslant x \leqslant \mu, \\
&= x - \mu & \mu \leqslant x \leqslant \mu + 1, \\
&= 0 & \text{all other } x.
\end{aligned}
\right\} \qquad (12.3)
$$

148

This distribution is symmetrical about $x=\mu$, and therefore satisfies (12.1); the reader should sketch its form. Although $\bar{x}$ is a reasonable estimator of μ, the alternative function

$$x^* = \tfrac{1}{2}(x_{\max}+x_{\min}) \tag{12.4}$$

can be proved to be better, in that both are consistent (section 12.3) and unbiased (section 12.4) but, for large n, x^* is much less variable from sample to sample than $\bar{x}$. Proofs relating to this example will not be given, as development of general theory is more interesting.

Evidently some consideration of desirable criteria is needed. This leads to one of the fields of statistics that is both most difficult and most interesting for the mathematician; some of the points of logic involved are controversial. Only an outline is given here, and the mathematical argument is not fully rigorous.

First must come a more complete specification of the situation, and the introduction of some notation and terminology. In order to make explicit the parameters of a distribution, a general p.d.f. may be symbolised by

$$f(x|\theta_1, \theta_2, \ldots, \theta_k), \tag{12.5}$$

where θ_p ($p=1, 2, \ldots, k$) are all the parameters of the distribution; knowledge of the numerical value for every θ_p would identify a particular distribution as a member of the family having the general form (12.5). This function must of course satisfy (4.25), (4.26) for all permissible values of the θ_p. A Normal distribution, for example, is a member of the family

$$f(x|\theta_1, \theta_2) = \frac{1}{\sqrt{(2\pi\theta_2)}} \exp\left\{-\frac{(x-\theta_1)^2}{2\theta_2}\right\}, \tag{12.6}$$

in which $\theta_2>0$.

Suppose that x_i ($i=1, 2, \ldots, n$) are n observations randomly and independently selected from the distribution specified by (12.5). The general problem is to devise rules of calculation from the x_i that will give quantities t_p ($p=1, 2, \ldots, k$) which can be regarded as estimating the corresponding θ_p. Little will be said here on distributions with $k>1$, as the case of one unknown parameter provides enough problems for an elementary discussion; of course this includes, for example, the distribution in (12.6) with *either* θ_1 or θ_2 known.

The presentation here is in terms of continuous variates, but of course essentially the same problems arise with a discrete variate. For example,

$$f(x|\theta_1, \theta_2) =$$
$$\binom{n}{x}\frac{\left\{\theta_1(\theta_1+\theta_2)(\theta_1+2\theta_2)\ldots(\theta_1+\overline{x-1}\theta_2)(1-\theta_1)(1-\theta_1+\theta_2)\ldots\right\}}{1(1+\theta_2)(1+2\theta_2)\ldots(1+\overline{n-1}\theta_2)} \tag{12.7}$$

6

is a possible p.d.f. for the probability of x successes in n non-independent trials, where $0 \leqslant \theta_1 \leqslant 1$, $0 \geqslant \theta_2 \geqslant -1/n$. For $\theta_2 = 0$, this becomes the binomial distribution; that it is a p.d.f. under more general conditions is shown in (A93–A98).

In some circumstances, interest may lie not so much in the θ_i as initially specified but in known functions of these such as $\log \theta_1$, $\sqrt{\theta_2}$, $(\theta_1 - \theta_2^2)/\theta_3$. Sometimes the formulation of a distribution is made more convenient for mathematical manipulation, or more directly relevant to the quantities to be studied, by adoption of a different parameterisation; for example, if in (12.6) one writes

$$\left. \begin{aligned} \theta_2 &= 1/\phi_2^2 \\ \theta_1 &= \phi_1/\phi_2 \end{aligned} \right\}, \tag{12.8}$$

the p.d.f. can be expressed

$$f(x|\phi_1, \phi_2) = \frac{\phi_2}{\sqrt{(2\pi)}} \exp\{-\tfrac{1}{2}(\phi_2 x - \phi_1)^2\}. \tag{12.9}$$

A *statistic* (cf. section 3.8) is defined to be any quantity calculated from the observations $x_1, x_2, \ldots, x_n$ in the sample according to a rule that has been specified exactly before the sample is taken. The symbol t, which *in this chapter* must not be confused with that introduced in section 9.10 and used in the 't test' (section 10.2), will signify a general statistic; it may be written more fully as $t(x_1, x_2, \ldots, x_n)$. Examples of possible rules for specifying a statistic are:

(i) $t = \bar{x}$,
(ii) $t = \sum (x_i - \bar{x})^2$,
(iii) $t = \sum x_i^4 / (\sum x_i^2)^2$,
(iv) $t = $ value of x_i for which $|x_i|$ is a maximum,
(v) $t = $ arithmetic mean of x_i^3 for all $x_i > 0\cdot5$,
(vi) $t = \max (|x_i - x_j|)$,
(vii) $t = $ one of x_i selected at random,
(viii) $t = \sum \log (1 + |x_i - \bar{x}|)$,
(ix) t is to be chosen to minimise $\sum |x_i - t|$.

If the p.d.f. of x is known, that of any statistic t will be determinate. More generally, for repeated random samples of n observations, t will have a p.d.f. dependent upon the parameters (or some of the parameters) in the p.d.f. of x, and in theory capable of being found from knowledge of the mathematical form of (12.5). Examples have been given in earlier chapters. Often the mathematical technology required to reduce the p.d.f. of t to manageable form is difficult or wholly intractable, as it usually would be for such as (iii) or (viii) above, although it can always be written in terms of assemblies of sums and integrals.

12.2 ESTIMATION

The requirement for estimating an unknown parameter θ might be that a statistic t be defined in such a way as to be the 'best' value that can be stated for θ on the evidence of the n observations alone. The criteria to be imposed in order that t shall be optimal are about to be discussed, and clearly must involve definition of 'best'. The criteria cannot require reference solely to the particular set of observations, because the observations themselves cannot provide both the estimator and the standards by which its quality is to be judged. Since θ is unknown, the sample can no more tell by how much a calculated statistic deviates from θ than it can tell the exact value of θ itself. Instead, $t(x_1, x_2, \ldots, x_n)$ must be seen as a rule of calculation for *any* set of n observations, and its success in estimation must be judged by its *average* performance over all possible samples of n. Moreover, one usually expects to specify t by a rule that is applicable for any size of sample (n), or at any rate for any number of observations above some minimum for which the problem degenerates. This is not strictly a theoretical requirement; situations exist in which t may have slightly different forms when n is odd and when n is even, or for some other classification of values of n.

It is usual to speak of t as an *estimator* (cf. section 3.8) when it is being regarded as a rule of calculation applicable to any set of observations, but to speak of a particular numerical value of t as an *estimate*. Thus, in (9.9)

$$s^2 = \Sigma (x_i - \bar{x})^2/(n-1) \tag{12.10}$$

defines s^2 as an estimator of σ^2, but the calculation in section 9.9 leads to

$$s^2 = 13 \cdot 37$$

as a particular estimate of σ^2.

Values of t determined in this fashion are often described as *point estimates*, to emphasise the fact that they attempt simply to provide single numerical values that are to be regarded as optimal. Often this seems a little paradoxical, since there is little reason to believe that the true value of the parameter is exactly estimated. If the mean height of 25 male students chosen at random from the 3126 matriculated at a university is 173·4 cm, this may be regarded as an estimate of the mean height of all the students; however, one will scarcely imagine that the result of measuring the 3126 students and averaging their heights would be particularly likely to give exactly 173·4 cm, rather than 173·2 cm or 173·5 cm. This awkwardness may be avoided by the use of *interval estimates*, statements that an unknown parameter lies between specified upper and lower limits. There are several ways in which a probability can be associated with such an interval. Examples of the calculation of fiducial and confidence limits have been given in sections 6.8, 8.5, and 10.2, and in Exercise 9.6. Equations (10.6), in particular, show the method of calculation of an interval estimate from two statistics, $\bar{x}$ and s, obtained from the observations.

12.3   CONSISTENCY

If t is an estimator of θ for all n, one desirable condition is that, in some probabilistic sense, t should tend to θ as n increases without limit. One cannot simply require that θ should be the limit of t in the ordinary mathematical sense, for t need not have a limit; except for trivial situations, for any finite n there will be a non-zero probability that t differs from θ by at least a stated amount. However, the condition can be expressed as follows:

For any fixed ϵ, however small,

$$Pr(|t-\theta| < \epsilon) \to 1 \quad \text{as } n \to \infty. \tag{12.11}$$

Such a t is said to be a *consistent* estimator of θ.

Those who are accustomed to formal statements of mathematical limit theory may prefer to express this more fully:

A necessary and sufficient condition for t to be a consistent estimator of θ is that for any fixed ϵ, η, however small, there exists n^*, a function of ϵ, η, such that

$$Pr(|t-\theta| < \epsilon) > 1-\eta \quad \text{for every } n > n^*. \tag{12.12}$$

Admirable though this is as a definition, it is not easily applied as a criterion for determining whether a particular statistic is consistent. An alternative necessary and sufficient condition can be expressed in terms of the mean and variance of t, obtained by considering the variation of t over all possible samples from the population. By definition, the first two moments of t are

$$\mu_1(t) \equiv E(t) = \int\int \ldots \int tf(x_1)f(x_2)\ldots f(x_n) \, dx_1 \, dx_2 \ldots dx_n, \tag{12.13}$$

$$\mu_2(t) \equiv \text{Var}(t) = \int\int \ldots \int [t-\mu_1(t)]^2 f(x_1)f(x_2)\ldots f(x_n) \, dx_1 \, dx_2 \ldots dx_n; \tag{12.14}$$

although these appear more complicated than anything previously discussed, they are in full accord with section 4.9. It can then be proved (A99–A102) that t is a consistent estimator of θ if and only if

$$\mu_1(t) \to \theta \quad \text{as } n \to \infty, \tag{12.15}$$

$$\mu_2(t) \to 0 \quad \text{as } n \to \infty, \tag{12.16}$$

where (12.15), (12.16) involve limits in the ordinary mathematical sense.

A requirement that t be a consistent estimator of θ does not uniquely determine t. For example, if θ is the mean of a Normal distribution, then $\bar{x}$, the arithmetic mean of the sample, is a consistent estimator of θ. However, so also is the *median* of the sample, defined in section 12.5. So also is the statistic

$$\sum x_i/(n + 23 \cdot 1). \tag{12.17}$$

Indeed, more generally, if t is a consistent estimator of θ in any distribution, so also are all the members of the family

$$t(1 + a_1 n^{-1} + a_2 n^{-2} + a_3 n^{-3}) \tag{12.18}$$

for fixed finite a_1, a_2, a_3.

12.4 UNBIASEDNESS

The requirement of consistency ensures that a statistic is estimating θ, rather than 7θ, $\log(\theta + 2)$, or some other function of this and other parameters, at any rate if the sample is sufficiently large. However, it tells nothing about the behaviour of t for small n. In practice, an estimator may be known to be consistent but the minimal value of n needed to secure reasonable approach to θ may be large or unknown.

A statistic is said to be an *unbiased* estimator of θ if

$$E(t) = \theta \quad \text{for all } n, \tag{12.19}$$

where $E(t)$ is as defined in (12.13). The difference $[E(t) - \theta]$ is termed the *bias* of t as an estimate of θ.

The most obvious example of an unbiased estimator is $\bar{x}$, the arithmetic mean of the sample of n observations; provided that the first moment of the distribution of the x_i exists (cf. section 6.4), $\bar{x}$ is an unbiased estimator of that moment whatever the form of the distribution. Similarly s^2 as defined by (9.9) is an unbiased estimator of the second moment of the distribution of x_i provided only that this moment exists. On the other hand, V defined by (9.6) is a consistent but biased estimator of this second moment.

Consistency may be regarded as unbiasedness of the limit for large samples, and usually unbiasedness in finite samples is a more stringent condition. However, there exist unbiased estimators that are not consistent. For example, statistic (vii) in section 12.1 is undoubtedly an unbiased estimator of the mean whatever the distribution; it is not consistent because its variance, being the variance of a single observation, is independent of n and does not satisfy (12.16). Again, for the Cauchy distribution (section 6.4), $\bar{x}$ is an unbiased estimator of the parameter c in (6.13), but it is not consistent since its distribution is identical with that of x; an alternative simply calculated statistic, the median (see section 12.5), is unbiased and consistent.

In the practical use of statistical techniques, a small bias in estimation seldom matters much, and consistency may be much more important. The limitations of the criterion of unbiasedness become apparent when various functions of a parameter are of interest; even though t is an unbiased estimator of θ, $\log t$ or $\sqrt{t}$ will not usually be unbiased estimators of $\log \theta$ or $\sqrt{\theta}$, whereas consistency is usually maintained over such transformations. For example, although s^2 is an unbiased estimate of σ^2, the variance of the distribution of the x_i, s is not in general an unbiased estimator of σ (A103–A105).

12.5 AN ILLUSTRATION

Consider the distribution whose p.d.f. is

$$f(x|\theta) = \frac{1}{\theta}e^{-x/\theta} \quad \text{for } x \geqslant 0. \tag{12.20}$$

For a sample of n, write

$$t_1 = \bar{x} = \sum x_i/n. \tag{12.21}$$

Elementary integration of xf and $x^2 f$ (A106–A110) easily proves that

$$E(t_1) = \theta, \tag{12.22}$$

$$\text{Var}(t_1) = \theta^2/n \to 0 \quad \text{as } n \to \infty. \tag{12.23}$$

Hence t_1 satisfies (12.15), (12.16), (12.19) and is therefore both a consistent and an unbiased estimator of θ.

Now write t_2 for another commonly used statistic which, like the mean, gives a general indication of the location of the sample on the scale of x. This statistic, the *median*, is defined as the middle value of the sample. More exactly, if the observations are written in order of magnitude from smallest to largest and for some integer, m, $n=2m+1$, t_2 is the $(m+1)$th in order; if $n=2m$, t_2 is the mean of the mth and the $(m+1)$th. Only

$n = 2m+1$ is discussed in detail here, $n = 2m$ being analysable similarly. Somewhat laborious integration (A111–A117) shows that

$$E(t_2) = \theta \sum_{m+1}^{2m+1} \frac{1}{j}. \tag{12.24}$$

In consequence of (A118–A119),

$$E(t_2) \to \theta \log_e 2 \quad \text{as } n \to \infty. \tag{12.25}$$

The p.d.f. (12.20) is not symmetrical, and therefore not surprisingly the middle observation is both biased and inconsistent as an estimator of θ. Also from the integration

$$\text{Var}(t_2) = \theta^2 \sum_{m+1}^{2m+1} \frac{1}{j^2} \tag{12.26}$$

$$< \frac{\theta^2}{m+1} \to 0 \quad \text{as } n \to \infty. \tag{12.27}$$

These results may be used to illustrate the construction of a consistent and an unbiased estimator from one that has neither property. Define

$$t_3 = t_2/\log_e 2. \tag{12.28}$$

By (12.25), (12.27),

$$E(t_3) \to \theta, \tag{12.29}$$

and

$$\text{Var}(t_3) \to 0, \quad \text{as } n \to \infty. \tag{12.30}$$

Therefore, by (12.15), (12.16), t_3 is a consistent estimator of θ, although it is still biased. On the other hand, the statistic t_4, defined by

$$t_4 = t_2 \Big/ \sum_{m+1}^{2m+1} \frac{1}{j}, \tag{12.31}$$

is equally easily seen to be an unbiased and consistent estimator of θ.

Thus t_1 and t_4 both possess the two properties regarded as desirable for an estimator of θ. Since unbiasedness and consistency do not uniquely determine an estimator, additional criteria can and should be introduced.

12.6 PRECISION

Both unbiasedness and consistency are conditions that the statistic t shall in some sense estimate the right quantity. However, t is not likely to be exactly equal to θ, and the next aspect of the problem that suggests itself for study is the closeness of the approach to θ. As mentioned in section 12.1, a statistic t will itself have a frequency distribution in repeated samples of n from the distribution of x. Examples of the derivation of such distributions have already been presented in sections 6.3, 9.5, 9.10, but the mathematical difficulties involved in obtaining the distribution of a statistic are often much greater than for these.

Suppose that t_1, t_2 are both unbiased and consistent estimators of θ. Each will have its own frequency distribution, and the choice between the statistics should rest upon a comparison of their p.d.f.'s. For this purpose, the most interesting characteristic of the p.d.f. is some measure of its dispersion around θ; a natural rule is to regard t_1 as preferable to t_2 if the distribution of t_1 shows less dispersion about θ than does that of t_2. Although dispersion need not be measured in terms of squared deviations, certain theoretical results about the asymptotic form of distributions in large samples (sections 6.2, 12.12) indicate this as particularly suitable as well as convenient. Hence t_1 will be preferred to t_2 if

$$Var(t_1) < Var(t_2). \qquad (12.32)$$

Commonly such an inequality goes in the same direction for every possible n, but there is no logical objection to employment of a criterion that makes t_1 preferable for some sample sizes, t_2 preferable for others. When (12.32) is satisfied, t_1 is said to be a more *precise* estimator of θ than t_2.

In some practical situations, an estimator may not be ruled out on account of a small bias, provided that it is consistent. A natural adaptation is then to replace (12.32) by

$$E[(t_1 - \theta)^2] < E[(t_2 - \theta)^2]. \qquad (12.33)$$

The bias will be defined as

$$b_t(\theta) = E(t) - \theta, \qquad (12.34)$$

where $b_t(\theta)$ is a function of n which tends to zero as $n \to \infty$. It follows that

$$E[(t - \theta)^2] = Var(t) + [b_t(\theta)]^2 \qquad (12.35)$$

essentially by the reasoning of (9.14).

In statistical usage, the word 'precision' always relates to the closeness of agreement between results from independent samplings of a distribution; it represents the extent to which independently determined numerical values of a statistic agree with one another, not necessarily with the parameter (if t happens to be a biased estimator of θ). In order to avoid confusion, the word should never be used to describe the numerical accuracy of arithmetic. Still more exactly, the *precision* of any statistic t (whether unbiased or biased) is defined to have the numerical value

$$\text{Precision of } t = 1/Var(t). \tag{12.36}$$

12.7 EFFICIENCY

The *relative efficiency* of two estimators of the same parameter, if both are unbiased, is defined to be the ratio of their precisions. Thus

$$\text{Efficiency of } t_2 \text{ relative to } t_1 = Var(t_1)/Var(t_2). \tag{12.37}$$

The concept of relative efficiency is especially useful in large samples: although both variances tend to zero as n increases, their ratio may have a non-zero limit. Indeed, variances of statistics are commonly proportional to n^{-1} in large samples (just as the variance of an arithmetic mean is proportional to n^{-1} whatever the sample size—section 5.5). The relative efficiency of two statistics then becomes the inverse ratio of numbers of observations necessary in order to achieve equal precision. This limiting ratio, the *asymptotic relative efficiency*, is often employed as a primary indicator of which of two or more alternative estimators is to be preferred; care must be exercised because of the possibility that the ordering may be different when n is not very large.

Evidently an estimator that is not consistent has asymptotic relative efficiency zero relative to any consistent estimator of the same parameter.

As an example, consider the Normal distribution $N(\theta_1, \theta_2)$, whose p.d.f. is specified in (12.6). Symmetry suffices to show that both the arithmetic mean, $t_1 \equiv \bar{x}$, and the median, t_2 (as defined in section 12.5), are unbiased estimators of θ_1. By (5.28)

$$Var(t_1) = \frac{\theta_2}{n}. \tag{12.38}$$

Evaluation of $Var(t_2)$ is a complicated piece of mathematics, of which nothing is presented here; in large samples, the result is approximately

$$Var(t_2) \doteqdot \frac{\pi\theta_2}{2n}, \tag{12.39}$$

but for small n the formula is more complicated. By (12.16), t_1 and t_2 are consistent, and by (12.37) the asymptotic efficiency of t_2 relative to t_1 is $2/\pi$. Table 12.1 shows the relative efficiency for small n. As noted in section 12.5, the median has to be separately defined for n odd and n even. The efficiencies for $n = 1, 3, 5, \ldots$, decline steadily towards $2/\pi$, as do those for $n = 2, 4, 6, \ldots$, but when the two series are written together an oscillation is introduced.

TABLE 12.1

Efficiency of median relative to mean as estimator of population mean in samples of n from $N(\theta_1, \theta_2)$

n	1	2	3	4	5	6	7	8
Rel. eff.	1·000	1·000	0·743	0·838	0·697	0·775	0·679	0·743

n	9	10	50	100	Limit
Rel. eff.	0·669	0·722	0·653	0·645	0·637

The meaning of the limiting value for the efficiency is that, for large n, the median of n observations from a Normal distribution is only as precise as the mean of $0·637n$ observations; to use the median instead of the mean is on average equivalent to discarding the information provided by 36·3 per cent of the observations and taking the mean of the remainder.

12.8 FINDING AN ESTIMATOR

So far, discussion has been concerned solely with the properties of particular estimators that have been already defined as functions of the observations. Suggestions have been made for comparing the merits of two defined estimators of the same parameter, but nothing has been said on how to find a statistic suitable for use as an estimator in a new situation.

The role of intuition and common sense must not be neglected, at least as directing attention to certain classes of statistic. Suppose that θ is a *parameter of location*; by this phrase is meant a parameter such that if the numerical measures of x are subjected to a linear transformation the value of θ is changed by the same transformation. If a, b are constants and

$$x^* = ax+b, \qquad (12.40)$$

then

$$\theta^* = a\theta+b \qquad (12.41)$$

is the parameter in the distribution of x^* corresponding to θ in the distribution of x. For example, if x is a temperature measured in °C, any parameter θ also measured in °C will be a parameter of location if a change to measurement of temperature in °K or °F replaces θ by $(\theta+273)$ or $(1·8\theta+32)$. This would be so if θ were the mean or the lower limit of the frequency distribution of x. For estimating such a θ, it will be natural to restrict attention to statistics with the same transformational properties, examples being the mean or median of a sample of observations or the mean of the five smallest observations. A proposal to estimate

θ by the difference between the largest and smallest observations, their ratio, or $\sum x^3$ for the sample would seem intuitively silly.

Again suppose that θ is a *parameter of scale*; this means that if x^* is defined by (12.40) then

$$\theta^* = a\theta \qquad (12.42)$$

is the parameter in the distribution of x^* corresponding to θ. In the temperature example, the change to °K or °C would replace θ by θ or $1\cdot8\theta$ respectively. For estimating θ, it will now be natural to restrict attention to statistics with this property, examples being the S.D., the range (i.e. the difference between the largest and smallest observations), or the mean value of $|x_i - \bar{x}|$.

By a slight extension of ideas, variances and higher moments of a distribution may be regarded as generalised scale parameters, at least where their representation as single parameters seems appropriate. However, a parameter of a distribution of a continuous variate need not be simply classifiable as a location or scale parameter. For a discrete variate, these notions are usually inapplicable. Where considerations of this kind can be applied, they usually admit a large number of possible estimators and the problem of choosing between them remains. At best, the necessary conditions for a valid estimator of a parameter of a specified frequency distribution are very loose, and one might surely hope for some more direct procedure for identifying a good estimator.

How then is one to find a good estimator of a particular parameter that occurs in a frequency distribution of specified form? The considerations advanced above may serve to exclude some statistics but will always leave open a wide choice. If any interest at all attaches to different values of n, the number of observations from which the statistic is to be calculated, consistency is likely to be regarded as a condition that must be fulfilled. Unbiasedness is generally considered to be a desirable property of an estimator, but less important provided that any bias is small relative to the S.E. of the estimator. In sections 9.2, 12.5 and Exercise 12.3 can be found examples of simple adjustments to estimators that remove bias without upsetting consistency, and devices of this kind are adopted where practicable. Usually many alternative consistent and either unbiased or approximately unbiased estimators can be proposed for one estimation problem, and choice between them can be based upon additional criteria. Even ease of computation can be a relevant criterion, but theoretical studies are more concerned with preferring an estimator because its value is likely to be close to that of the parameter; in particular, high precision of the estimator may be wanted.

Sections 12.9–12.11 describe three principles that have been widely used for the discovery of estimators. Although these are presented primarily in terms of a single unknown parameter, all generalise to problems with two or more parameters and the differences between them then increase in importance.

*12.9   METHOD OF MOMENTS

The moments of a distribution (section 4.9) in general are functions of the parameters. From a sample of n observations, numerical values known as *sample moments* may be calculated exactly as if the sample were itself a complete population. For example, in the obvious notation to correspond with μ'_i and μ_i,

$$m'_1 = \frac{1}{n} \sum x_i, \qquad (12.43)$$

$$m'_2 = \frac{1}{n} \sum x_i^2, \qquad (12.44)$$

$$m_3 = \frac{1}{n} \sum (x_i - \bar{x})^3. \qquad (12.45)$$

If the first k moments of a distribution with k unknown parameters are equated to the corresponding sample moments, the resulting equations can be solved in order to give values for the parameters. (The possibility of multiple roots will not be discussed, as it is rarely important.) The method is fairly obviously consistent, but need not be unbiased. For example, V in (9.6) is identical with m_2; this statistic was shown to be a biased estimator of μ_2, which might be taken as a parameter of the distribution.

The method of moments has been found useful in some circumstances where alternatives seemed mathematically intractable. It breaks down if some moments do not exist, and investigation of the bias and precision of the estimators can be very difficult.

12.10   METHOD OF LEAST SQUARES

A method of greater intrinsic interest, though not applicable in all situations to which the method of moments can be applied, depends upon minimising the sum of squares of deviations of observations from expectation; it was used extensively by Gauss (1777–1855). For a single parameter, one determines

$$E(x) = \int x f(x|\theta) \, dx \qquad (12.46)$$

as in (4.30). If this is a function of θ, one then considers the expression $S(\theta)$ defined by

$$S(\theta) = \sum [x_i - E(x_i)]^2, \tag{12.47}$$

and determines t as the numerical value of θ that minimises $S(\theta)$. Evidently differentiation rapidly leads to

$$E(x) = \bar{x}, \tag{12.48}$$

and estimation of θ is exactly as by the method of moments. Unfortunately in the simple situation so far described only one parameter can be estimated: the method will not lead to any estimator for θ_2 of (12.6) whether θ_1 is already known or not.

The compensation lies in the possibility of estimation in a more complicated situation. Suppose that the x_i do not all come from one frequency distribution although the same parameter θ occurs in the expectation of each x_i. For example, $E(x_i)$ may depend upon the value, u_i, of a variate u measured simultaneously with x_i: u_i could be the weight of an animal for which x_i is a measure of physiological performance, or u_i could be the time that a piece of machinery has been in use before a measurement x_i is made upon it (cf. section 12.17). One might have a relation such as

$$E(x_i) = \theta u_i, \tag{12.49}$$

or

$$E(x_i) = e^{-\theta u_i^2}. \tag{12.50}$$

Whether the u_i are all equal, all different, or fall into several groups of equal values, $S(\theta)$ can be defined by (12.47); minimisation with respect to θ may now be a less trivial procedure, and may demand numerical rather than algebraic procedures, but it will still provide an estimator for θ.

Another advantage of the method of least squares is its easy extension to estimation of several parameters. The example in section 11.12, as described in (A84–A92), involved 16 parameters (in addition to σ^2), with two linear relations between them, each of the 32 observations having as its expectation (A85) a different linear combination of the parameters. Application of the method of least squares leads rapidly to estimates of the parameters; indeed, each τ_k is estimated by the mean of the eight observations for the corresponding treatment, and similar simple results follow for the other parameters (A120–A123). Even if the set of observations comes from a less symmetrical experiment (for example, if accidents caused 3 of the 32 observations wanted in section 11.12 either not to be made or to be lost from the records), the method of least squares remains applicable, although the equations that express the conditions for S to be a minimum are then less easy to solve.

To base estimation upon attempts to keep the values of $[x_i - E(x_i)]$ small in absolute magnitude is intuitively reasonable. Other non-negative functions, such as

$$\sum [x_i - E(x_i)]^4$$

or

$$\sum |x_i - E(x_i)|,$$

might have been chosen for minimising, but considerations relating to the central limit theorem and the frequent occurrence of squared differences in statistical theory favour the sum of squares. In general, the method leads to consistent estimators, and of course the minimising of $S(\theta)$ secures some sort of optimality in respect of precision. In many important instances, the method is identical with that of section 12.12.

If the x_i do not all have the same variance, the method should be modified by minimising a weighted sum of squares; equation (12.47) is replaced by

$$S(\theta) = \sum \frac{[x_i - E(x_i)]^2}{Var(x_i)}. \tag{12.51}$$

An important weakness of the method is that it is not invariant under transformation of the measurements. A rate of uptake of oxygen by the blood would usually be measured by a variate x expressed as weight of oxygen per unit time. However, it would be no less logical to use a variate y expressed as time required for uptake of unit weight; some types of instrumentation would most readily give x, others y. Evidently

$$y = C/x \tag{12.52}$$

where C is a constant, and the frequency distribution of y will involve the same parameter or parameters as that of x although the mathematical form will be different. However

$$E(y) \neq C/E(x), \tag{12.53}$$

and, more important, minimisation of $\sum [y_i - E(y_i)]^2$ will not lead to the same estimator of a parameter θ as does minimisation of $\sum [x_i - E(x_i)]^2$. For some types of data, there is an inherent arbitrariness in the particular function that happens to be measured, and for the estimator of a parameter to depend upon this function is usually undesirable (A124–A129).

12.11   LIKELIHOOD

For a sample of n observations from a distribution with p.d.f. $f(x|\theta)$, the *likelihood* (of the sample) is defined to be

$$L(\theta) = Cf(x_1|\theta).f(x_2|\theta)...f(x_n|\theta). \tag{12.54}$$

Exact definition of the constant C is unimportant (A130), but it must be independent of θ. For many purposes, the logarithm of the likelihood is a more useful function:

$$\log L(\theta) = \log C + \sum_{i=1}^{n} \log f(x_i|\theta). \qquad (12.55)$$

Note that the chief interest of the likelihood lies in considering it as a function of θ, though of course it also has an implicit dependence upon the x_i.

12.12 METHOD OF MAXIMUM LIKELIHOOD

Another intuitively reasonable procedure for estimating θ is to maximise $L(\theta)$. That is to say, an estimator t_L is obtained as a solution of

$$dL(\theta)/d\theta = 0. \qquad (12.56)$$

Although t_L as so defined is a function of the observations x_i, commonly it cannot be expressed in explicit functional form. The equations for maximum likelihood estimators (like those for least squares estimators) often require to be solved by iteration or other techniques of successive numerical approximation, the labour of which has been much reduced by modern computing machinery.

The existence of multiple roots of (12.56) is seldom a problem. The most common situation is that the equation has only one solution, except for irrelevancies such as $\theta = 0$ or a value outside the meaningful range. Moreover, the nature of the likelihood function is such as usually to ensure that if it has only one extremum this is a maximum.

The estimator t_L has a number of properties that certainly entitle it to be considered as among the best possible, and indeed it may reasonably be claimed as the best for practical use in a wide variety of situations. Among these properties are:

(i) t_L is a consistent estimator of θ;
(ii) in large samples, t_L is 'most efficient', in the sense that for any other consistent estimator, t,

$$\frac{Var(t_L)}{Var(t)} \to \text{Limit} \leqslant 1 \qquad (12.57)$$

as $n \to \infty$;
(iii) if x is transformed to a new variate y by a single-valued function involving no unknown parameters,

$$y = h(x), \qquad (12.58)$$

(12.52) and (A124) being examples, and $f(x|\theta)$ is expressed as a p.d.f. for y instead of x, the value of t_L is unaltered;

(iv) as n becomes large, the distribution of t_L in repeated sampling tends to Normality;

(v) if $f(x|\theta)$ is a distribution that possesses a *sufficient estimator* (section 12.16) for θ, then t_L is sufficient.

Of these, (i) and (iii) are intuitively fairly obvious when written as formal mathematical statements. The truth of (ii) follows by proving that as n becomes large $Var(t_L)$ tends to the minimum specified by the Cramér–Rao inequality (section 12.14). Proofs of these and of the somewhat more difficult theory underlying (iv) are not presented. The statement (v) receives further comment in section 12.16.

As will be seen later, sufficiency is a particularly desirable property. Even when it is not achievable, the maximum likelihood estimator is at least very good and usually relatively simple to employ in large samples. Unfortunately, the question of how large n must be for efficiency of t_L to be high and for a Normal distribution to be a satisfactory approximation is not easily answered; indeed, its difficulty causes it to be too often neglected in statistical practice. For small n, alternative estimators are sometimes more satisfactory, especially if their distributional properties can be more easily studied.

Note that t_L is not necessarily unbiased, but sometimes a minor adjustment will remove bias in small samples without affecting large sample properties. For example, applying the obvious generalisation to the two parameters of the Normal distribution, (12.6),

$$\log L(\theta_1, \theta_2) = -\tfrac{1}{2}n\log 2\pi - \tfrac{1}{2}n\log\theta_2 - \sum \frac{(x_i - \theta_1)^2}{2\theta_2}, \quad (12.59)$$

rapidly leads to (A131–A132)

$$t_1 = \bar{x}, \quad (12.60)$$

$$t_2 = \sum (x_i - \bar{x})^2/n, \quad (12.61)$$

as a result of equating the two differential coefficients to zero. Here t_1 is an unbiased estimator of θ_1; t_2 is a biased estimator of θ_2 which is easily adjusted so as to eliminate the bias (9.6–9.9).

Note also that, like the method of least squares, the method of maximum likelihood readily generalises to problems with several parameters, and to problems in which the x_i do not all come from the same frequency distribution. The example in section 11.12 may be considered from this point of view also. If each x_{ijk} is Normally distributed about ξ_{ijk} with variance σ^2 the same for all observations, the logarithm of the likelihood will have as the only terms involving the ρ, γ, τ parameters (see A85)

$$-\Sigma\,(x_{ijk}-\rho_i-\gamma_j-\tau_k)^2/2\sigma^2. \qquad (12.62)$$

Hence so far as these parameters are concerned, maximisation of likelihood is equivalent to minimisation of S in (A120) and thus is equivalent to the method of least squares. On the other hand, estimation of σ^2 by maximum likelihood leads to a bias as in (12.61). This equivalence of maximum likelihood and least squares obtains in a wide range of problems, and aids the justification of least squares when an approximate Normality of distribution is a reasonable assumption.

12.13 EXAMPLES

Sometimes maximum likelihood leads to very simple estimators. One instance is the distribution specified by (12.20). For a sample of n independent observations,

$$\log L(\theta) = -n\log\theta-\Sigma\,x_i/\theta. \qquad (12.63)$$

Differentiation gives as the equation for the estimator

$$-\frac{n}{t_L}+\frac{\Sigma\,x_i}{t_L^2} = 0, \qquad (12.64)$$

whence

$$t_L = \Sigma\,x_i/n. \qquad (12.65)$$

Next consider the p.d.f. (for $\theta\geqslant0\cdot5$)

$$\left.\begin{aligned} f(x|\theta) &= \frac{2}{\Gamma(\theta)}\,e^{-x^2}x^{2\theta-1} \quad (x\geqslant0)\\ &= 0 \quad\quad\quad\quad\quad (x<0) \end{aligned}\right\} \qquad (12.66)$$

The fact that this satisfies (4.26) follows from (9.16) with $z=x^2$. For this p.d.f.

$$\log L(\theta) = n\log2-\Sigma\,x_i^2-n\log\Gamma(\theta)+(2\theta-1)\,\Sigma\,\log x_i. \quad (12.67)$$

Differentiation with respect to θ and equation to zero gives

$$\frac{d\Gamma(t_L)}{dt_L} = \frac{2\,\Sigma\,\log x_i}{n}. \qquad (12.68)$$

Study of the gamma function shows that $d\Gamma(w)/dw$ is a monotonic single-valued function of w, which has in fact been tabulated; consequently, t_L is easily obtained from (12.68).

Thirdly consider the Cauchy distribution (section 6.4) with the p.d.f.

$$f(x|\theta) = \pi^{-1}[1+(x-\theta)^2]^{-1}. \tag{12.69}$$

The equation for maximising the likelihood is

$$\sum \frac{x_i-t_L}{1+(x_i-t_L)^2} = 0, \tag{12.70}$$

which can be written as a polynomial equation of degree $(2n-1)$. The appropriate solution can be found by any standard numerical technique for solving equations; iterative procedures, in which a preliminary guess at the solution is improved by successive approximations to as high a numerical accuracy as is desired, are commonly needed with maximum likelihood estimation.

*12.14 THE CRAMÉR–RAO INEQUALITY

An interesting and very important theorem states the minimum variance that may be manifested by an unbiased estimator of a parameter θ. Like the central limit theorem (and like many theorems of pure mathematics), it is 'usually' true under reasonable conditions of continuity and differentiability of various functions but the ingenious mathematician can devise situations under which it breaks down. Exact statement can take various forms, but no very rigorous version is appropriate here; essentially the theorem is:

If x_i for $i=1, 2, \ldots, n$ represents a sample of n independent observations from a frequency distribution with p.d.f. $f(x|\theta)$, and if t is *any* statistic for which

$$E(t) = \theta, \tag{12.71}$$

then

$$[Var(t)]^{-1} \leqslant -n \int f(x|\theta) \frac{d^2}{d\theta^2} [\log f(x|\theta)] \, dx, \tag{12.72}$$

where integration is over the whole range of the distribution.

A reasonably simple proof requires that the limits of the range of the distribution, e.g. (0, 1) or $(-\infty, +\infty)$, be themselves independent of θ and that the mathematical form of $f(\ )$ be such as to permit inversion of the order of various integrations and differentiations.

The right-hand side of (12.72) is necessarily positive, and the theorem therefore sets a non-zero lower limit to $Var(t)$. The proof is outlined elsewhere (A133–A157). Note that the lower limit is inversely proportional to n, since apart from the factor n the expression in (12.72) is independent of sample size. Property (ii) of maximum likelihood estimators stated in section 12.12 can in fact be supplemented by the stronger result that, for a sample from any distribution, as n becomes large $Var(t_L)$ approaches asymptotically or is actually equal to the lower limit set by (12.72). With the usual replacement of integrals by sums, the theorem also holds for discrete distributions.

As one simple illustration, consider the Normal distribution (12.6) under the condition that θ_2 is known and only θ_1 must be estimated. Then, writing f as an abbreviation for $f(x|\theta)$,

$$\log f = -\tfrac{1}{2}\log(2\pi\theta_2) - \frac{(x-\theta_1)^2}{2\theta_2}, \tag{12.73}$$

and

$$\frac{d^2}{d\theta^2}(\log f) = -\frac{1}{\theta_2}. \tag{12.74}$$

According to the theorem, any unbiased estimator of θ_1 must have

$$[Var(t)]^{-1} \leqslant \int \theta_2^{-1} f(x|\theta_1, \theta_2)\,dx$$

$$= n/\theta_2. \tag{12.75}$$

Hence

$$Var(t) \geqslant \frac{\theta_2}{n}. \tag{12.76}$$

Of course $\bar{x}$ is the maximum likelihood estimator and has a variance equal to the lower bound for all n.

The Cauchy distribution produces a less trivial integration. From (12·69) it is easily proved that (A158–A160)

$$\frac{d^2}{d\theta^2}(\log f) = \frac{2}{1+(x-\theta)^2} - \frac{4}{[1+(x-\theta)^2]^2}. \tag{12.77}$$

The integral required for (12.72) is not difficult (A161–A162); the result is

$$Var(t) \geqslant \frac{2}{n}. \tag{12.78}$$

*12.15 INFORMATION

The quantity

$$I = -\int f \frac{d^2}{d\theta^2}(\log f)\,dx$$

$$= -E\left[\frac{d^2}{d\theta^2}(\log f)\right] \tag{12.79}$$

evidently has an additive property for samples of all sizes, in that nI is the reciprocal of the minimal variance for the class of unbiased estimators. This total, nI, is termed the *amount of information* on θ contained in the sample; I itself is known as the *intrinsic accuracy* of the distribution in respect of θ.

*12.16 SUFFICIENCY

An important class of distributions has the property that a statistic calculated from a sample can extract and summarise the total information on a particular parameter. Suppose that T, a statistic defined as a function of the x_i, is an unbiased estimator of θ for all n, and that

$$Var(T) = 1/nI. \tag{12.80}$$

Thus T is an estimator that always achieves the lower bound for its variance and may be regarded as obtaining all the information on θ present in the sample.

A somewhat less rigid expression of the same idea is to say that a statistic T (as before, defined for all n but no longer necessarily unbiased) is *sufficient* for θ if every other statistic t calculated from the sample is such that its frequency distribution conditional on T is independent of θ. In other words, for any fixed T, all probabilities associated with the distribution of t are unaffected by θ; therefore, when T is known to take a particular value, additional knowledge of the value of t tells nothing further about the likely values of θ, *and this is true for every possible t*. Thus T contains all the information on θ present in the sample. Any monotonic function of T will have the same property. The statistic first encountered may not itself be a very desirable estimator of θ; however, a search may then be made for a function of T that is either unbiased or approximately unbiased (consistency is a consequence of section 12.15). An unbiased sufficient estimator may be proved to have the property (12.80).

The criterion for sufficiency may seem difficult to apply, because it implies examination of every possible t. However, an alternative condition which is usually more easily applied can be shown to be equivalent.

No proofs of any of these results will be given here, nor of the following statement relating to maximum likelihood. If a distribution possesses a statistic sufficient for a parameter θ, then the maximum likelihood estimator of θ is sufficient. Of course, (ii) of section 12.12 implies that as n becomes large the maximum likelihood estimator tends asymptotically to comply with (12.80), but the statement now made is that the estimator will achieve minimum variance in finite samples if a sufficient statistic exists.

12.17 REGRESSION

In connection with both least squares and maximum likelihood, mention has been made of observations in which values of a variate may differ in frequency distribution or in expectation although the same parameters are involved throughout. Of particular importance in this context are situations in which the parameters determine relations between two or more variates. The theory of *regression* is concerned with one variate whose distribution depends upon values of one or more other variates, these latter values being *either* imposed by an investigator as part of his control over the circumstances of an experiment (e.g. dose of a drug, time for which experimental material is exposed to a particular influence) *or* measured by an investigator with negligible error of measurement as part of the background influencing the first variate (e.g. age of a mouse whose reaction to radiation is to be studied, percentage of carbon in a mineral oil whose surface tension is to be studied).

More specifically perhaps the most important problem of this type concerns a variate, x, whose expectation for a fixed value of another variate, u, is a linear function of u:

$$E(x|u) = \alpha + \beta u, \tag{12.81}$$

where α, β are unknown parameters. The data consist of observations x_i ($i=1, 2, \ldots, n$), for each of which the corresponding u_i is known; estimation is possible for any sample in which not all the u_i are equal. Equation (12.81) is termed the *linear regression equation* of x on u. If nothing more than this is specified, the parameters α, β may be estimated by least squares, this requiring minimisation of

$$S(\alpha, \beta) = \sum_i (x_i - \alpha - \beta u_i)^2, \tag{12.82}$$

the two-parameter analogue of (12.47).

A more complete specification of the problem that is often appropriate is to state that the frequency distribution of x for fixed u is $N(\alpha + \beta u, \sigma^2)$. The logarithm of the likelihood of the sample is (cf. 12.59)

$$\log L(\alpha, \beta, \sigma) = -\tfrac{1}{2}n \log 2\pi - n \log \sigma - \sum (x_i - \alpha - \beta u_i)^2 / 2\sigma^2. \tag{12.83}$$

Maximisation of $L(\alpha, \beta, \sigma)$ with respect to α, β is then equivalent to minimisation of $S(\alpha, \beta)$. Simultaneous estimation of σ or σ^2 introduces a bias of the usual kind, for which adjustment can be made by taking account of degrees of freedom, but this is not the primary interest here.

For least squares or maximum likelihood, the estimators of α, β can be written

$$a = \bar{x} - b\bar{u}, \tag{12.84}$$

$$b = \Sigma \, (x_i - \bar{x})(u_i - \bar{u})/\Sigma \, (u_i - \bar{u})^2, \tag{12.85}$$

where of course

$$\bar{x} = \Sigma \, x_i/n, \quad \bar{u} = \Sigma \, u_i/n, \tag{12.86}$$

and Σ everywhere denotes summation over the n observations (A163–A167). For the Normal distribution model, the estimators satisfy a generalised condition of sufficiency.

These estimators have certain minimal variance properties, whether or not the frequency distribution of x is Normal. If the requirement that the variance of x is constant be relaxed, further complications enter. The simplest extension is to the case of the variance of x being a *known* function of u, say $g(u)$. Equation (12.83) is then replaced by

$$\log L(\alpha, \beta) = -\tfrac{1}{2}n \log 2\pi - \tfrac{1}{2}\Sigma \, g(u_i) - \sum \frac{(x_i - \alpha - \beta u_i)^2}{2g(u_i)}, \tag{12.87}$$

and only the parameters α, β require estimation. Maximisation of the likelihood is equivalent to minimisation of

$$S(\alpha, \beta) = \sum \frac{(x_i - \alpha - \beta u_i)^2}{g(u_i)}, \tag{12.88}$$

and thus is the same as minimising a weighted sum of squares as defined in (12.51).

Again for the Normal distribution with constant variance, the maximum likelihood estimator of σ^2 is readily proved to be

$$V = \Sigma \, (x_i - a - bu_i)^2/n. \tag{12.89}$$

However, by algebra more complicated than but analogous to that of section 9.2, the expectation of V can be shown to be

$$E(V) = (n-2)\,\sigma^2/n. \tag{12.90}$$

Therefore V is biased, but

$$s^2 = \Sigma \, (x_i - a - bu_i)^2/(n-2) \tag{12.91}$$

is unbiased. None of this algebra is presented.

Evidently both (12.81) and the Normal distribution are stating that the mean value of x for fixed u is linearly related to u. An index of the

closeness with which individual points are concentrated about this line
is provided by the *correlation coefficient*, defined as

$$r = \frac{\sum (x_i - \bar{x})(u_i - \bar{u})}{[\sum (x_i - \bar{x})^2 \sum (u_i - \bar{u})^2]^{\frac{1}{2}}}. \qquad (12.92)$$

With the exception of the arithmetic mean, perhaps no statistic has been
as extensively used as the correlation coefficient. Despite its unquestion-
able importance, it is commonly abused and many fallacious arguments
have been based upon it. Here comment will be limited to a warning
against too facile acceptance of uncritical inferences.

These procedures can be generalised to take account of a non-linear
dependence of x on u and also of situations in which several variates
like u must be taken into account simultaneously. It is important to
note that the correlation coefficient is relevant only when there is
linearity.

12.18   STATISTICAL INFERENCE

To end this chapter, some brief notes about various important types of
statistical inference seem desirable.

Most of the chapter so far has been concerned with point estimation
(section 12.2): effort is concentrated on defining and fulfilling optimal
conditions for the calculation of a single numerical value that will 'best'
estimate an unknown parameter. In a sense this is unrealistic. If one is
interested in a parameter representing the mean height (in cm) of adult
males in a population, a sample of 100 might lead to the estimate 172·30,
but one would scarcely believe that this was appreciably more likely to
represent the exact truth than 172·28 or 172·314. Even if 1000 or 10000
men were measured, the arithmetical outcome of the estimation process
would not enjoy any special advantage over closely neighbouring values.
Similarly, if interest lies in a parameter defined as the proportion of
defective electric switches of model AB produced by a factory, and a
sample of 200 includes 5 defectives, the point estimate of the parameter,
0·025, is scarcely preferable to neighbouring values such as 0·027 or
0·0228. The finding of 500 defectives in 20000 might modify the plausi-
bility of 0·027 as an alternative to 0·025 but would not affect the logical
principle. Only very seldom does a numerical value for a point estimate
possess some unique superiority over every possible alternative.

Why then is the process of obtaining a point estimate regarded with
any favour? Despite its weaknesses, it does most concisely summarise
the evidence of the sample on a single issue: there are occasions when

convenience demands that just one value be quoted. Moreover, if the point estimate can be supplemented by a standard error, this serves to indicate broadly what range of values can be regarded as plausible alternatives to the estimate. Concepts such as precision and efficiency, although introduced as properties of the point estimate, are in fact concerned with the amount of variation that might be encountered among repeated determinations of the estimate, and therefore contribute to understanding about alternative plausible values.

Nothing will alter the central importance of point estimators. Nevertheless, several other aspects of inference from a set of observations need comment, since each is important in some circumstances. These may be entitled:

> Confidence inference,
> Fiducial inference,
> Prior and posterior probabilities,
> Decision making.

The practice of statistics has been harmed by extravagant claims that one of these is ideal for all purposes, and choice between them has sometimes been dictated by fashion rather than by wisdom.

The brevity of sections 12.19–12.22 is not an indication of their importance: more thorough discussion would be too complicated for the present purpose.

*12.19   Confidence Inference

Statistical techniques find many practical applications in the manufacturing industries, and of these one large class is the control of the quality of products. For example, batches of like articles may be produced, and the manufacturer may wish for an assurance (or be required by law to give an assurance) that the average weight per article is not less than a stated limit (e.g. packages of a foodstuff), that the average working life exceeds a stated number of hours (e.g. an electrical component), or that the percentage of defective items is below a certain figure.

Here the notion of confidence limits indicates the kind of protection that statistics can give. Suppose that for a particular set of observations an estimator t of a parameter θ takes the numerical value t_0. One may enquire 'What true values of θ are not seriously in conflict with the observational evidence that t_0 summarises?' A value θ_L might be determined such that, if $\theta = \theta_L$, the probability that a set of observations collected in the same manner gives $t \geqslant t_0$ is 0·05. Fairly obviously, if the true θ were less than θ_L the probability of so large a value for t would be less than 0·05. Thus θ_L separates values of θ too small to be plausible (as indicated by a probability 0·05) from those not too small in relation to the observational evidence; θ_L is termed the lower single-tailed *confidence limit* at probability 0·95 $(=1-0\cdot05)$. Of course, the user can choose whatever probability he wishes. Having calculated such a θ_L, he will reasonably conclude that the true θ for the population from which his observations came is not less than θ_L, and he may adopt this as the basis of statements about the quality of his product.

The calculations require knowledge of the distribution of t for fixed θ or an adequate approximation to this. Examples of particularly simple type have been given in sections 6.8, 9.9, 10.7; the reader must not confuse the statistic t now defined as an estimator of θ with the standard symbol used in the t distribution!

As explained in sections 6.6–6.8, single-tailed upper confidence limits can be similarly defined and calculated by appropriate reversals of inequalities; double-tailed limits are also obtainable as there explained, and in practice are often required.

*12.20 FIDUCIAL INFERENCE

An alternative system of inference, not easily distinguished from the confidence type in simple situations but having logical differences that become great in more complicated situations, seeks to express a probability distribution for θ in terms of a known t. The confidence argument, as implied by section 12.19, is very suitable for assessing whether or not a batch of canned food or of transistors is up to a required quality. Scientific research, however, is much less concerned with questions of this kind than with summarising the evidence about a parameter in a concise form suitable for combination with, or discussion in relation to, that from other sources. There is seldom any requirement that a hypothesis about θ be finally accepted or rejected, more commonly a need for continually summarising information from new experiments or other observations.

As an example, suppose that x is distributed as $N(\theta, 3)$; a known variance is stated in order to keep the problem simple. If a sample of n is taken, and the statistic

$$t = \bar{x} \tag{12.93}$$

is formed, then the distribution of t is $N(\theta, 3/n)$. That is to say, the p.d.f. of t is

$$\left(\frac{n}{6\pi}\right)^{\frac{1}{2}} \exp\left[-\frac{n(t-\theta)^2}{6}\right]. \tag{12.94}$$

By consideration of the behaviour of (12.94) as a function of θ for fixed t, one can invert the interpretation of this p.d.f. and, with the aid of a differential element $d\theta$, regard it as a p.d.f. for θ in terms of t. In other words, the parameter is regarded as having a distribution of the form $N(t, 3/n)$. This is termed the *fiducial distribution* of θ for given t. It expresses the information about θ from the sample of n in the form of probabilities measuring the strength of belief in the possible values.

From the fiducial distribution can be formed *fiducial limits* (single or double tailed), calculated to cut off tail areas of the distribution corresponding to stated probabilities. For this example, the fiducial limits are identical with confidence limits calculated with the same probabilities. This is often but not universally true.

The theory of fiducial inference is difficult and at present far from completely understood.

*12.21   PRIOR AND POSTERIOR PROBABILITIES

All discussion of quantitative statistical inference so far has related to the use of the data provided by an experiment or other sample of observations in accordance with mathematical theory but without reference to any other numerical values. Admittedly in some places a variance has been taken to have a numerical value already known (e.g. section 6.6), but this has been only a preliminary stage of the exposition, recognised as unrealistic and subsequently (e.g. section 10.2) replaced by an analysis dependent solely on the internal evidence of the data.

Consider the following somewhat artificial problem. There are two boxes each containing four pennies; box 1 has two pennies dated 1964 and two dated 1965, box 2 has three dated 1964 and one dated 1965. A box is chosen at random in such a way as to give box 1 probability P_1, box 2 probability $P_2 = 1 - P_1$. A subject who does not know which box has been chosen is allowed to shake the box, take out one coin, record the date, replace the coin, and repeat these actions twice more so as to have the dates for three independent drawings from the same chosen box. Of course, all coins are supposed sufficiently alike not to be distinguishable by touch, and coins with the same date cannot be distinguished by eye. The records are: 1964, 1964, 1964. What can be said about whether or not the chosen box was box 1 ?

The subject does not know whether he has seen the same coin three times or two or three different coins. If box 1 was chosen, the probability that he obtains a 1964 penny at any draw is $2/(2+2)$ or $\frac{1}{2}$. His three draws are independent, and therefore the probability for the actual records is (section 3.5)

$$Pr(X|1) = (\tfrac{1}{2})^3,\qquad(12.95)$$

where X is an abbreviation for the observations; similarly, if box 2 was chosen

$$Pr(X|2) = (\tfrac{3}{4})^3.\qquad(12.96)$$

Hence in repeated trials (a trial being choice of a box followed by recording of three dates) the relative frequency of a set of records identical with X (1964, 1964, 1964) is

$$(\tfrac{1}{2})^3 P_1 + (\tfrac{3}{4})^3 P_2,\qquad(12.97)$$

of which records of X from box 1 contribute

$$(\tfrac{1}{2})^3 P_1.\qquad(12.98)$$

These results can be regarded as a consequence of combining formulae relating to independent events (choice of a box and each of three choices of a coin within a box) and mutually exclusive events (the alternative boxes) as given in sections 3.4, 3.5. Alternatively, a trial may be represented in terms of a sample space of 16 points (really two alternatives in each of four dimensions) for all combinations of box 1, box 2 and 1964, 1965 at each draw. Therefore, conditional on X having been observed, the probability that the records came from box 1 is

$$Pr(1|X) = \frac{(\tfrac{1}{2})^3 P_1}{(\tfrac{1}{2})^3 P_1 + (\tfrac{3}{4})^3 P_2}.\qquad(12.99)$$

This simplifies to

$$Pr(1|X) = \frac{8P_1}{27 - 19P_1},\qquad(12.100)$$

but (12.99) displays better the origins of the formula. Evidently

$$Pr(1|X) = \begin{cases} 1 & \text{if } P_1 = 1 \\ 0 & \text{if } P_2 = 1 \\ 8/35 & \text{if } P_1 = P_2 = \tfrac{1}{2} \end{cases},\qquad(12.101)$$

this last being much smaller than P_1 as should be guessed from the fact that box 2 has a higher proportion of 1964 pennies.

The problem might have been phrased a little differently. A parameter θ must take one of the two values $\tfrac{1}{2}$ and $\tfrac{3}{4}$. Three observations are made from a binomial distribution in which θ is the probability that the observation is of type α (as alternative to δ); the results are α, α, α. It is known that the value of θ itself has been determined in such a way that, before any observations are made,

$$Pr(\theta = \tfrac{1}{2}) = P_1. \tag{12.102}$$

What can be inferred about θ after the observations? The answer, corresponding to (12.100), is

$$Pr(\theta = \tfrac{1}{2}) = \frac{8P_1}{27 - 19P_1}, \tag{12.103}$$

Here a statement such as (12.102), relating to initial knowledge, is termed a *prior probability*, and the result (12.103) is termed a *posterior probability*.

As described, the problem is artificial, but in fact it corresponds closely with the probabilistic inference required in genetical investigations. In the light of her heredity, the probability that a woman carries a recessive gene for some abnormality may be known, the prior probability. Her husband's genotype and the fact that she has borne three normal children may be evidence on which a posterior probability may be calculated as a revised assessment of her risk. Other such situations may arise in real life. If P_1 is known, a probability statement about the parameter, θ, results, and this has a greater logical content than the type of statement arising in confidence or fiducial inference.

Equation (12.99) is a particular case of *Bayes's theorem*, a direct consequence of considerations of conditional probability (section 3.3). More generally, suppose that a parameter θ takes the value θ_r with probability P_r $(r=1, 2, \ldots, R; \sum_r P_r = 1)$. Then P_r is termed the *prior probability* of θ_r. Observations X are made in such a way that the probability of X if $\theta = \theta_r$ is $Pr(X|\theta_r)$. The argument already presented generalises to give the probability that $\theta = \theta_r$ conditional on X being observed:

$$Pr(\theta_r|X) = \frac{Pr(X|\theta_r).P_r}{\sum_r Pr(X|\theta_r).P_r}. \tag{12.104}$$

This is the *posterior probability* that $\theta = \theta_r$. Together with a corresponding result for a continuous prior distribution for θ, in which probability elements and integrals replace discrete probabilities and sums, (12.104) is the general expression of Bayes's theorem.

This much is uncontroversial. Its utility depends entirely on knowledge of the prior probabilities, knowledge which every statistician would like to have and use but which is available only in special classes of problem and which indeed is often inconceivable. In recent years, some have sought to popularise extraordinary notions that where the prior probability distribution is unknown or even non-existent it can be invented so as to permit use of Bayes's theorem. Sometimes the 'justification' is quoted that the exact prior distribution postulated makes little difference to the conclusions; this is scarcely surprising if the observations are extensive, but surely suggests that one ought to be as well content without any such postulate. Sometimes a more axiomatic approach is adopted, such as asserting that in the absence of knowledge to the contrary all P_r may be taken as equal. If there is complete ignorance about the P_r, it is difficult to see how scientific understanding can be advanced by such an arbitrary postulate. Moreover, there are many circumstances in which no sense can be attached to the concept of a prior distribution. In Experiment TWO, for example, θ might be the true difference in rate of oxygen uptake between treatments A, D; how can any meaning be attached to a prior distribution of θ in the abstract, unless numerical knowledge of such a distribution exists? How can a postulated distribution, introduced as an aid to production of a posterior distribution, even approximately represent something that has no conceptual existence? If a man stands in a dark room that contains a mirror in an unknown position, what is the shape of his reflection?

When the concept of a prior distribution is meaningful, interesting and useful conclusions may sometimes emerge from the insertion of alternative specifications of this distribution. Much of what is currently advocated in this connection, however, goes far beyond this kind of exploratory process. Dignified by the name of *Bayesian inference*, ideas are advanced that are sophisticated versions and generalisations of those wisely rejected by earlier generations. Bayes (1702–61), an early student of probability theory, discussed the possibility that the theorem now bearing his name might be used as a basis for inference about parameters even in the absence of information expressible as prior probabilities. His proper doubts about the legitimacy of assumptions (such as an equal distribution of ignorance) from which a prior distribution could be constructed, and his consequent distrust of the logical validity of inferences about the parameters, caused him to refrain from publication during his lifetime. To attach the adjective 'Bayesian' to the methods currently popular in some circles seems at least as unfair as to describe a lung cancer as Ralegh's disease or to praise Bluebeard for his valiant support of monogamy!

Criticism must not be taken to mean that research into this type of inference is valueless; on the contrary, good students may find in it much that is interesting theoretically and beneficial to statistical practice. For example, in the planning of an experiment for estimating a certain quantity a parameter of some scientific system, the ideal conditions in respect of choice of experimental design, replication, and allied topics may depend greatly on the true value of the paramenter. Introduction of a prior distribution, however tentative and uncertain in meaning, to represent the investigator's ideas on the likely value of the parameter, can sometimes provide a good basis for optimal planning. Very different is any suggestion of making the inference drawn from the investigation—perhaps a probability statement about the parameter— depend materially on the prior distribution used. A great amount of work on the theory of such methods of inference is now in progress, and the already voluminous literature will grow rapidly. If the past is any guide to the future, an appreciable proportion of that literature will be nonsense but plenty of important ideas will emerge; the reader who has not been discouraged by the scathing remarks in the previous paragraph may perhaps one day contribute to sifting the wheat from the chaff.

*12.22 DECISION MAKING

Some experiments are undertaken in order to pick out the single best 'treatment' or a group of good treatments from a larger number. Twenty lubricants might undergo comparative tests in order to guide the choice of one for future use with a particular piece of machinery. Thirty-six new strains of barley might be compared (by growing them on small plots and measuring the produce) in order to select the three that seem best suited for further development as candidates for widespread sowing in Scotland. Two hundred and thirty applicants for clerical posts might all be given aptitude tests before twelve are chosen to fill the available vacancies.

In any such situation, errors may occur because good treatments (lubricants, employees, etc.) are discarded after test or because poor treatments are wrongly judged to be good and are accepted. Small standard deviations, good experimental design, and high precision are instrumental in reducing the probability of such errors, and standard errors need to be estimated if there is to be any assessment of the probabilities. On the other hand, significance tests are of no relevance, confidence and fiducial limits of little relevance. If the employer has 12 vacancies, he will take the 12 applicants who seem 'best', irrespective of whether the difference between numbers 12 and 13 is large or small (the fact that where aptitude differences are small he may also take account of looks and personality merely means a change in the scale of measurement of suitability on which the 12 best are to be chosen). In order to devise an optimal procedure for reaching these decisions, account also needs to be taken of the costs involved. Errors of judgement in appointing clerks might be reduced if each applicant were tested for 6 hours, but the value to be placed on choosing the best may not balance the cost of this testing in place of, say, a 20-minute test and a consequent greater risk of errors.

The view is sometimes advanced, explicitly or implicitly, that the whole of statistical practice can be comprised within decision theory. This can be grossly misleading. There is a sense in which the outlook is correct: analysis of statistical data may be followed by decisions whether or not to publish a report, whether to conduct a further experiment and, if so, how to plan it, whether or not to seek a new hypothesis to explain certain phenomena, and so on. But decisions like these in a context of 'pure' scientific research are somewhat different from decisions whether or not to pass a batch of electrical switches as up to standard for sale, whether or not the recent performance of a large machine makes withdrawal from service for overhaul a wise policy, whether or not to recommend replacement of an old drug by a new in the interest of efficacy in curing a certain disease, or which three out of 36 varieties of barley to recommend for further study or general use.

All decisions in the second group involve evaluating estimates of parameters in relation to costs of measurement, costs of further investigation, probabilities and costs of wrong or sub-optimal decisions, and values of the benefits that follow good decisions. The costs and values are not necessarily measured on a monetary scale, alternative scales for measuring human satisfaction or dissatisfaction sometimes being more appropriate. To these decisions, formal statistical decision theory is immensely valuable.

On the other hand, decisions in the first group have none of the same finality. The numerical value of a parameter does not make the difference between one action and its opposite, but perhaps merely strengthens belief in one scientific hypothesis instead of an alternative. Scientific hypotheses evolve rather than suffer clear acceptance or rejection. The corpus of quantitative scientific knowledge grows by accumulation of estimates of parameters, not so much by rigid tests of significance and consequent firm assertions on truth and falsehood. The development of decision theory is technically interesting and practically important as a branch of statistical inference, but no service is done by extravagant claims that the practice of statistical science should be seen solely from this point of view.

EXERCISES

12.1 For the p.d.f. in (12.20), find the efficiency of t_4 relative to t_1 in samples of $n=2m+1$. Evaluate this function numerically for $m=1, 2, 3, 4$. Show, by as crude an approximation as you wish, that the asymptotic relative efficiency lies between 0·24 and 0·96, or find closer bounds if you can.

12.2 If x, y, z are independent observations with variances σ_1^2, σ_2^2, σ_3^2 about a common expectation θ, prove that

$$u = ax+by+cz$$

has expectation $\theta(a+b+c)$. Subject to the condition

$$a+b+c = 1,$$

determine a, b, c so as to minimise $Var(u)$. Find the efficiency of the u defined by these a, b, c relative to that of u with any a, b, c for which $a+b+c=1$. State the corresponding results for two observations instead of three, and infer generalisations for k observations.

12.3 A dairy has in use a proportion P of cracked and defective milk bottles, and these are issued at random to customers. A housewife who buys one bottle a day resolves to complain when she has had a total of B defective bottles. She completes this total in n days. Prove that $(B-1)/(n-1)$ is an unbiased estimator of P. The housewife prefers to word her complaint that 'One in θ of the bottles is defective' where $\theta=1/P$. Prove that n/B is an unbiased estimator of θ. [Simple adaptation of binomial distribution required.]

12.4 The variate x has p.d.f. $\lambda e^{-\lambda x}$. Prove that, for a sample of n, any unbiased estimator of λ must have

$$Var(t) \geqslant 1/n\lambda^2.$$

Hence comment on maximum likelihood estimation of λ and on unbiased estimation of $1/\lambda$ (cf. section 12.5).

12.5 For a sample of n from the distribution $N(6, \sigma^2)$, prove that the maximum likelihood estimator of σ^2 is

$$\Sigma (x_i-6)^2/n,$$

and show that this estimator is unbiased.

12.6 Under the conditions of Exercise 12.5, prove that no unbiased estimator of σ^2 can have a variance smaller than $2\sigma^4/n$. By integration to find $E[(x_i-6)^4]$ or otherwise, prove that the maximum likelihood estimator has this variance.

12.7 For the Poisson distribution (section 5.7), the probability that the discrete variate takes the integer value r is

$$Pr(r) = e^{-\gamma}\gamma^r/r! \quad \text{for } r \geqslant 0.$$

A sample of n observations consists of values r_i $(i=1, 2, ..., n)$. Find the maximum likelihood estimator of γ, prove that it is unbiased, and find its variance.

12.8 *State* the Cramér–Rao inequality in respect of a variate with a discrete distribution, making clear both your notation and the summations used. Hence find the minimum variance that could be possessed by any estimator of γ in Exercise 12.7.

12.9 In Exercise 12.7, find the probability of a particular set of r_i *conditional on* $\sum r_i$ having the fixed value R, and show that for every set of r_i this probability is independent of γ. [This in fact ensures that R is a sufficient statistic for γ.] Investigate the frequency distribution of R, and show how to obtain from R a consistent and unbiased estimator of γ with minimum variance. [First obtain these results for $n=2$; then, if you can, generalise them.]

12.10 Plot x as ordinate against u as abscissa for each of the three following sets of values (three separate diagrams). For each set, use (12.84)–(12.86) to calculate a and b, and insert the estimated regression line on each diagram.

u	5	11	3	5	6
x	9	4	12	7	8

u	5	11	3	5	6
x	7	12	4	8	9

u	5	11	3	5	6
x	4	8	9	12	7

12.11 The variate x has p.d.f.

$$f(x) = \theta^{-1} \quad \text{for } 0 \leqslant x \leqslant \theta$$
$$= 0 \quad \text{elsewhere,}$$

θ being an unknown parameter. A sample of n independent observations, $x_1, x_2, ..., x_n$, is taken. You may of course now infer that θ is at least as great as the largest of the x_i. Show that

$$t = 2 \sum_{i=1}^{n} x_i/n$$

7

is an unbiased estimator of θ. By first finding the variance of a single x_i, determine $Var(t)$.

[Harvard, 1966]

12.12 In Exercise 12.11, let X be the largest member of the set of n observations. Prove that, for any specified X_0 $(0 \leqslant X_0 \leqslant \theta)$,

$$Pr(X \leqslant X_0) = (X_0/\theta)^n.$$

Hence find the p.d.f. of X, and prove

$$E(X) = \frac{n\theta}{n+1},$$

$$E(X^2) = \frac{n\theta^2}{n+2}.$$

Deduce that

$$u = X(n+1)/n$$

is an unbiased estimator of θ and find its variance.

[Harvard, 1966]

12.13 Discuss as fully as you can the theoretical and practical merits of the estimators t, u in Exercises 12.11, 12.12. Compare the two. Can you suggest situations in which each might have special advantages? Discuss any practical advice you can give on the utility of the estimators.

Appendix

MATHEMATICAL DEVELOPMENT

From (4.12),

$$\frac{d}{d\alpha} G(\alpha) = NP(Q+P\alpha)^{N-1} \tag{A1}$$

$$= NP(Q+P)^{N-1} \quad \text{when } \alpha = 1 \tag{A2}$$

and $Q+P=1$. A more pedestrian approach, from (4.13), is

$$E(r) = 0.f(0)+1.f(1)+2.f(2)+\ldots+N.f(N) \tag{A3}$$

$$= 0.Q^N+1.NQ^{N-1}P+2.\frac{N(N-1)}{2!}Q^{N-2}P^2+\ldots$$

$$= NP\left[Q^{N-1}+(N-1)Q^{N-2}P+\frac{(N-1)(N-2)}{2!}Q^{N-3}P^2+\ldots\right]$$

$$= NP(Q+P)^{N-1}$$

$$= NP. \tag{A4}$$

❋   ❋   ❋

The reader should verify (4.22) by the method of (A1–A2), but should note also the direct procedure usually required in situations for which the p.g.f. is not very tractable:

$$E[r(r-1)] = 0.Q^N+0.NQ^{N-1}P+2.\frac{N(N-1)}{2}Q^{N-2}P^2$$

$$+6.\frac{N(N-1)(N-2)}{3!}Q^{N-3}P^3+\ldots$$

$$= N(N-1)P^2[Q^{N-2}+(N-2)Q^{N-3}P+\ldots] \tag{A5}$$

$$= N(N-1)P^2(Q+P)^{N-2}$$

$$= N(N-1)P^2. \tag{A6}$$

Then, from (4.23),

$$E[(r-NP)^2] = N(N-1)P^2+NP-2N^2P^2+N^2P^2$$
$$= N^2P^2-NP^2+NP-N^2P^2$$
$$= NP(1-P). \tag{A7}$$

※   ※   ※

From (4.33)

$$\mu_2 = \int_{-\infty}^{\infty} (x^2-2\mu x+\mu^2)f(x)\,dx$$

$$= \int_{-\infty}^{\infty} x^2 f(x)\,dx - 2\mu \int_{-\infty}^{\infty} xf(x)\,dx + \mu^2 \int_{-\infty}^{\infty} f(x)\,dx$$

$$= \mu_2' - 2\mu'\mu + \mu^2. \tag{A8}$$

Similarly

$$\mu_k = \int_{-\infty}^{\infty} \left[x^k - k\mu x^{k-1} + \binom{k}{2}\mu^2 x^{k-2} - \ldots + k(-\mu)^{k-1}x + (-\mu)^k \right] f(x)\,dx$$

$$= \mu_k' - k\mu\mu_{k-1}' + \binom{k}{2}\mu^2 \mu_{k-2}' - \ldots + k(-\mu)^{k-1}\mu + (-\mu)^k, \tag{A9}$$

and the two last terms always coalesce into $-(k-1)(-\mu)^k$.

※   ※   ※

For a continuous variate, from (4.29),

$$M_x(\theta) = \int_{-\infty}^{\infty} e^{\theta x}f(x)\,dx$$

$$= \int_{-\infty}^{\infty} \left[1+\theta x+\frac{\theta^2 x^2}{2!}+\frac{\theta^3 x^3}{3!}+\ldots \right] f(x)\,dx$$

which, after integration term by term,

$$= 1+\mu\theta+\mu_2'\frac{\theta^2}{2!}+\mu_3'\frac{\theta^3}{3!}+\ldots. \tag{A10}$$

For a discrete variate, the same result follows when the integral is replaced by a summation.

※   ※   ※

Equation (4.45) requires some experience of change of variables in multiple integrals and the use of the Jacobian. Write

$$I = \int_{-\infty}^{\infty} K e^{-(x-\xi)^2/(2\sigma^2)} \, dx. \tag{A11}$$

Substitute

$$x = \xi + \sigma u. \tag{A12}$$

Then

$$I = \int_{-\infty}^{\infty} K \sigma e^{-\frac{1}{2}u^2} \, du. \tag{A13}$$

Take the product of two such integrals, and write as

$$I^2 = K^2 \sigma^2 \int_{-\infty}^{\infty} \int_{-\infty}^{\infty} e^{-\frac{1}{2}(u^2 + v^2)} \, du \, dv. \tag{A14}$$

Now regard u, v as rectangular co-ordinates, and transform to polar co-ordinates r, ϕ by

$$\left. \begin{aligned} u &= r \cos \phi, \\ v &= r \sin \phi, \end{aligned} \right\} \tag{A15}$$

Then

$$\frac{\partial(u, v)}{\partial(r, \phi)} = r. \tag{A16}$$

Since the integral (A13) is over the whole plane, the limits for r are 0, ∞ and those for ϕ are 0, 2π. Hence

$$\begin{aligned} I^2 &= K^2 \sigma^2 \int_0^\infty \int_0^{2\pi} r e^{-\frac{1}{2}r^2} \, dr \, d\phi \\ &= 2\pi K^2 \sigma^2 [e^{-\frac{1}{2}r^2}]_0^\infty \\ &= 2\pi K^2 \sigma^2. \end{aligned} \tag{A17}$$

✳   ✳   ✳

In the definition of $M_x(\theta)$ for this distribution, note that

$$x\theta - \frac{(x-\xi)^2}{2\sigma^2} = -\frac{1}{2\sigma^2}[x - (\xi + \sigma^2\theta)]^2 + \xi\theta + \sigma^2 \frac{\theta^2}{2}.$$

Hence

$$M_x(\theta) = K \exp\left[\xi\theta + \frac{\sigma^2\theta^2}{2}\right] \int_{-\infty}^{\infty} \exp\left[-\frac{1}{2\sigma^2}(x - \xi - \sigma^2\theta)^2\right] dx; \tag{A18}$$

(4.47) follows because the integral in (A18) is simply $1/K$, as follows by substituting

$$x = \xi + \sigma^2 \theta + \sigma u. \tag{A19}$$

❋   ❋   ❋

If an infinite series, S, has the form

$$S = 1 + a_1 \theta + a_2 \theta^2/2! + a_3 \theta^3/3! + \ldots, \tag{A20}$$

then

$$\frac{d^k S}{d\theta^k} = a_k + a_{k+1} \theta + a_{k+2} \theta^2/2! + \ldots \tag{A21}$$

and substituting $\theta = 0$ gives a_k.

❋   ❋   ❋

A well-known mathematical approximation, known as Stirling's formula, enables the numerical value of $m!$ to be obtained with high accuracy for fairly large m; it states

$$\log(m!) = \tfrac{1}{2}\log 2\pi + (m + \tfrac{1}{2})\log m - m. \tag{A22}$$

❋   ❋   ❋

For continuous variates, with u defined by (5.17),

$$
\begin{aligned}
E(u) &= \int\int (x_1 + x_2) f(x_1, x_2)\, dx_1\, dx_2 \\
&= \int\int x_1 f(x_1, x_2)\, dx_1\, dx_2 + \int\int x_2 f(x_1, x_2)\, dx_1\, dx_2 \\
&= E(x_1) + E(x_2),
\end{aligned}
\tag{A23}
$$

and a parallel demonstration holds for discrete variates.

❋   ❋   ❋

A commonly required procedure in the handling of m.g.f.'s is to expand them as power series and to rearrange or otherwise manipulate the terms of these series. Two simple examples occur in section 5.5. That leading to (5.26) should be obvious. By definition of central moments (section 4.9), the statement (5.27) can be written in series. The right-hand side can then be regarded as a binomial of the form $(1 + u)^n$. Expansion of this to three terms only ensures that all terms up to θ^4 are retained, and coefficients of powers of θ^2, θ^3, θ^4 are then collected. The main steps are

$$\left[1+\mu_2\frac{\theta^2}{2n^2}+\mu_3\frac{\theta^3}{6n^3}+\mu_4\frac{\theta^4}{24n^4}+\dots\right]^n$$

$$= 1+n\left(\mu_2\frac{\theta^2}{2n^2}+\mu_3\frac{\theta^3}{6n^3}+\mu_4\frac{\theta^4}{24n^4}+\dots\right)$$

$$+\frac{n(n-1)}{2}\left(\mu_2\frac{\theta^2}{2n^2}+\dots\right)^2$$

$$= 1+\mu_2\frac{\theta^2}{2n}+\mu_3\frac{\theta^3}{6n^2}+\mu_4\frac{\theta^4}{24n^3}$$

$$+\mu_2^2\frac{(n-1)\theta^4}{8n^3}+\dots. \tag{A24}$$

A little heavier labour would enable $\bar{\mu}_5$, $\bar{\mu}_6$ to be obtained similarly.

⁂   ⁂   ⁂

Rather simpler than (A24) are the expansions leading to (5.37), (5.39), but the idea is the same. From (5.35),

$$M_x(\theta) = \exp\left[\mu\left(\theta+\frac{\theta^2}{2!}+\frac{\theta^3}{3!}+\dots\right)\right]. \tag{A25}$$

This may be expanded term by term in an exponential series

$$M_x(\theta) = 1+\mu\left(\theta+\frac{\theta^2}{2}+\frac{\theta^3}{6}+\dots\right)+\tfrac{1}{2}\mu^2\left(\theta+\frac{\theta^2}{2}+\frac{\theta^3}{6}+\dots\right)^2$$

$$+\tfrac{1}{6}\mu^3\left(\theta+\frac{\theta^2}{2}+\frac{\theta^3}{6}+\dots\right)^3+\dots \tag{A26}$$

$$= 1+\mu\theta+\theta^2(\tfrac{1}{2}\mu+\tfrac{1}{2}\mu^2)+\theta^3(\tfrac{1}{6}\mu+\tfrac{1}{2}\mu^2+\tfrac{1}{6}\mu^3)+\dots \tag{A27}$$

by locating the appropriate power of θ in each term of (A26).

⁂   ⁂   ⁂

From (6.3)

$$\log[M_t(\theta)] = n\log\left[M_{x-\mu}\left(\frac{\theta}{\sqrt{(n\mu_2)}}\right)\right]$$

$$= n\log(1+A), \tag{A28}$$

where, by substitution in (6.4),

$$A = \frac{\theta^2}{2n} + \frac{\mu_3}{(n\mu_2)^{\frac{3}{2}}} \cdot \frac{\theta^3}{6} + \dots \tag{A29}$$

But

$$\log(1+A) = A - \frac{A^2}{2} + \frac{A^3}{3} - \dots \tag{A30}$$

Expansion of each term and rearrangement in powers of θ shows

$$\log[M_t(\theta)] = n\left[\frac{\theta^2}{2n} + \frac{\mu_3}{(n\mu_2)^{\frac{3}{2}}} \frac{\theta^3}{6} + \text{terms with factors } n^{-2}, n^{-\frac{5}{2}}, \dots\right]. \tag{A31}$$

In this kind of argument, convergence of series is seldom a worry because θ can be regarded as arbitrarily small.

※   ※   ※

If

$$z = cy + d, \tag{A32}$$

where y is a variable and c, d are constants, combination of (4.40), (4.41) shows that

$$M_z(\theta) = e^{d\theta} M_y(c\theta). \tag{A33}$$

In particular, if y has the distribution $N(\xi, \sigma^2)$,

$$M_y(\theta) = \exp\left[\xi\theta + \sigma^2\frac{\theta^2}{2}\right] \tag{A34}$$

and therefore

$$M_z(\theta) = \exp\left[(c\xi + d)\theta + c^2\sigma^2\frac{\theta^2}{2}\right]; \tag{A35}$$

consequently z has the distribution $N(c\xi + d, c^2\sigma^2)$.

※   ※   ※

In (6.13), write

$$u = x/\sqrt{b}. \tag{A36}$$

Then

$$\int_{-\infty}^{\infty} f(x)\,dx = \int_{-\infty}^{\infty} \frac{a/\sqrt{b}}{1 + \left(u - \dfrac{c}{\sqrt{b}}\right)^2}\,du$$

$$= \frac{a}{\sqrt{b}}\left[\tan^{-1}\left(u - \frac{c}{\sqrt{b}}\right)\right]_{-\infty}^{\infty}$$

$$= \pi a/\sqrt{b}, \tag{A37}$$

and (4.26) leads to (6.14).

※   ※   ※

As a simple illustration, suppose that $n=11$, $n_1=6$, $n_2=5$, and renumber the rats so that those on treatment A are numbers 1, 2, ..., 6. Then evidently orders such as

$$1, 6, 3, 5, 2, 4, 10, 11, 9, 8, 7, \tag{A38}$$

and
$$6, 4, 1, 3, 2, 5, 7, 11, 9, 10, 8, \tag{A39}$$

(6!5! of them in all) are obviously the most extreme in their indication that A is associated with increased rate of oxygen uptake. The orders

$$1, 6, 3, 5, 10, 2, 11, 4, 9, 8, 7 \tag{A40}$$

and
$$6, 4, 1, 3, 7, 2, 11, 5, 9, 10, 8 \tag{A41}$$

must obviously be regarded as equal to one another in the degree of extremeness but definitely less extreme than (A38) and (A39). No one would be likely to question the statement that

$$1, 6, 3, 10, 5, 2, 11, 4, 9, 8, 7 \tag{A42}$$

is still less extreme than (A40) and (A41). But is

$$1, 6, 3, 5, 10, 11, 2, 4, 9, 8, 7 \tag{A43}$$

more or less extreme than (4.42)? Either opinion could be defended, and even more difficult decisions must be faced. In order to avoid any temptation to adjust a test in a direction favourable to the user's wishes, it is essential that before experimental results are examined a rule shall have been agreed for deciding which of two orders is the more extreme or whether the two are ranked as equally extreme. This rule must be applicable unambiguously to every pair out of the $n!$ possible orders. Formulation of such a rule is easier than it may sound, and most reasonably sensible rules will lead to the same conclusions from significance tests in the majority of instances.

※　　　　※　　　　※

Under the conditions of Theorem III, in terms of moment generating functions, (4.41) gives

$$M_{a_i x_i}(\theta) = M_{x_i}(a_i \theta), \tag{A44}$$

Therefore, by (5.22), since (4.34) shows the second moment (μ_2') of x_i to be $(\sigma_i^2 + \xi_i^2)$,

$$M_X(\theta) = \prod_{i=1}^{n} [1 + a_i \xi_i \theta + \tfrac{1}{2} a_i^2 (\sigma_i^2 + \xi_i^2) \theta^2 + \ldots] \tag{A45}$$

$$= 1 + \theta \sum a_i \xi_i + \tfrac{1}{2} \theta^2 [\sum a_i^2 \sigma_i^2 + (\sum a_i \xi_i)^2] + \ldots \tag{A46}$$

whence (8.3), (8.4) follow with the aid of a second use of (4.34).

※　　　　※　　　　※

Strictly, the minimisation of the expression (8.7) subject to the condition (8.1) ought to take account of the fact that n_1, n_2 must be integers. Although general procedures for maximising functions under such a constraint can be troublesome, with a function as simple as (8.7) it will suffice to neglect the restriction to integers. Using (8.1),

$$\sigma_X^2 = \frac{\sigma_1^2}{n_1} + \frac{\sigma_2^2}{n-n_1}. \tag{A47}$$

Differentiation leads to the equation for an extremum

$$-\frac{\sigma_1^2}{n_1^2} + \frac{\sigma_2^2}{(n-n_1)^2} = 0 \tag{A48}$$

or

$$\frac{n_1}{\sigma_1} = \frac{n_2}{\sigma_2} = \frac{n}{\sigma_1+\sigma_2}. \tag{A49}$$

The second differential coefficient readily shows this to be a minimum. Moreover, there is no difficulty in proving that if n_1, n_2 must be integers the minimum must be given by one of the pairs of integers on either side of (A49) and usually by the nearer pair. In practice, σ_X^2 is so 'flat' in the neighbourhood of (A49) that the exact minimum does not matter.

The method of Lagrange multipliers gives a more symmetrical and elegant derivation of (A49).

❋ ❋ ❋

Derivation of (9.7) is a simple instance of a type of manipulation wanted often in the algebra of statistics, which depends greatly on properties of sums of squares. Care is needed in the use of $E(\ )$ and Σ operations. By (4.19) and (9.4),

$$E\left[\sum_{i=1}^{n} (x_i-\xi)^2\right] = \sum_{1}^{n} E[(x_i-\xi)^2]$$

$$= \sum_{1}^{n} \sigma^2$$

$$= n\sigma^2. \tag{A50}$$

Again, since $\bar{x}$ is constant so far as the Σ operation is concerned,

$$E[\Sigma (x_i-\xi)(\bar{x}-\xi)] = E[(\bar{x}-\xi) \Sigma (x_i-\xi)]$$

$$= E[(\bar{x}-\xi)(n\bar{x}-n\xi)]$$

$$= E[n(\bar{x}-\xi)^2]$$

$$= n\, Var\,(\bar{x})$$

$$= n(\sigma^2/n) \tag{A51}$$

by (5.28). Also $\quad E\left[\sum (\bar{x}-\xi)^2\right] = E\left[n(\bar{x}-\xi)^2\right]$

$$= n(\sigma^2/n) \tag{A52}$$

by (5.28). The result then follows.

❀ ❀ ❀

The identity in section 9.3 also requires care with $\sum$. Remember that $\sum_1^n$ of a constant is equal to n times the constant! Therefore

$$\sum (x_i-\bar{x})^2 = \sum (x_i^2-2\bar{x}x_i+\bar{x}^2)$$
$$= \sum x_i^2-2\bar{x}\sum x_i+\sum \bar{x}^2$$
$$= \sum x_i^2-2(\sum x_i/n)\sum x_i+n(\sum x_i/n)^2$$
$$= \sum x_i^2-(\sum x_i)^2/n. \tag{A53}$$

❀ ❀ ❀

Equation (9.17) follows immediately from (9.16) by substitution of $w=1$. Equation (9.18) requires integration by parts:

$$\Gamma(w+1) = \int_0^\infty z^w e^{-z}\,dz$$

$$= [-z^w e^{-z}]_0^\infty + w \int_0^\infty z^{w-1} e^{-z}\,dz$$

$$= 0+w\Gamma(w). \tag{A54}$$

Values of the gamma function when the argument is a half-integer are also easily found. Consider first $w=\frac{1}{2}$, and

$$\Gamma(\tfrac{1}{2}) = \int_0^\infty z^{-\frac{1}{2}} e^{-z}\,dz.$$

Substitute $\quad z = \tfrac{1}{2}u^2$

and thus replace dz by $u\,du$; then

$$\Gamma(\tfrac{1}{2}) = \int_0^\infty \frac{\sqrt{2}}{u} e^{-\frac{1}{2}u^2} u\,du$$

$$= \frac{1}{\sqrt{2}} \int_{-\infty}^\infty e^{-\frac{1}{2}u^2}\,du \quad \text{by symmetry}$$

$$= \pi^{\frac{1}{2}} \tag{A55}$$

by reference to (A11–A17). By use of (9.18), the function can be evaluated for $w = 3/2, 5/2, 7/2, \ldots$. In general, numerical integration is needed for the evaluation of $\Gamma(w)$, but extensive tables have been calculated and published. Thus the mathematician may write $\Gamma(4 \cdot 73)$ and mean a particular numerical value readily obtainable from a table just as he would write $\log(4 \cdot 73)$. The approximation (A22) is applicable to $\Gamma(m+1)$ without restriction to integers.

✳   ✳   ✳

In the integral for $M_{(x_i - \xi)^2}(\theta)$, write

$$\theta - \frac{1}{2\sigma^2} = -\frac{1}{2\lambda^2}. \tag{A56}$$

Then

$$M_{(x_i - \xi)^2}(\theta) = \frac{\lambda}{\sigma} \int_{-\infty}^{\infty} \frac{1}{\lambda\sqrt{(2\pi)}} \exp\left[-\frac{(x-\xi)^2}{2\lambda^2}\right] dx$$

$$= \lambda/\sigma \quad \text{from (A11–A17) again}$$

$$= (1 - 2\sigma^2 \theta)^{-\frac{1}{2}} \quad \text{by (A56).} \tag{A57}$$

✳   ✳   ✳

There are several ways of proving the independence of distribution of the expressions $\sum (x_i - \bar{x})^2$ and $n(\bar{x} - \xi)^2$ in equation (9.24), under the condition that each x_i is $N(\xi, \sigma^2)$, and of obtaining the distribution of $\sum (x_i - \bar{x})^2$. That most commonly given involves what is known as an *orthogonal transformation* of the x_i, so as to give a set of n independently distributed transformed values, each of which is $N(0, \sigma^2)$ and one of which equals $n^{\frac{1}{2}}(\bar{x} - \xi)$. An alternative is by use of moment generating functions.

For simplicity of notation, write

$$u_i = (x_i - \xi)/\sigma. \tag{A58}$$

The probability that a randomly selected observation x_i occurs in the range $(u_i, u_i + du_i)$ is (from 5.42),

$$\frac{1}{\sqrt{(2\pi)}} e^{-\frac{1}{2}u_i^2} du_i. \tag{A59}$$

Since the n observations are independent, the probability that observation i lies in $(u_i, u_i + du_i)$ for $i = 1, 2, \ldots, n$ is, by generalisation of (3.8),

$$(2\pi)^{-n/2} e^{-\frac{1}{2}\sum u_i^2} du_1 du_2 \ldots du_n. \tag{A60}$$

Now (9.24) may be written

$$\sum u_i^2 = \sum (u_i - \bar{u})^2 + n\bar{u}^2 \tag{A61}$$

by rearrangement of (9.12), where

$$\bar{u} = \sum u_i/n. \tag{A62}$$

The m.g.f. of $\sum (u_i - \bar{u})^2$ may be found in the usual manner, by way of an expectation over the distribution for which (A60) is the p.d.f.:

$$M_{\sum(u_i - \bar{u})^2}(\theta) = E[e^{\theta \sum (u_i - \bar{u})^2}]$$

$$= (2\pi)^{-\frac{1}{2}n} \int \int_{-\infty}^{\infty} \cdots \int \exp [\theta \sum (u_i - \bar{u})^2 - \tfrac{1}{2} \sum u_i^2]$$

$$du_1 \, du_2 \ldots du_n. \tag{A63}$$

Of course, multiple integration is needed in order to find the expectation over the distribution of all the u_i simultaneously. The exponent in the integrand may be written:

$$-\tfrac{1}{2}[(1-2\theta) \sum u_i^2 + 2n\theta\bar{u}^2] \quad \text{by (A61)}$$

$$= -\tfrac{1}{2}\left[(1-2\theta) \sum u_i^2 + \frac{2\theta}{n}(\sum u_i)^2\right]$$

$$= -\tfrac{1}{2}\left[\left(1-2\theta\frac{n-1}{n}\right) \sum u_i^2 + \frac{4\theta}{n} \sum_{i<j} \sum u_i u_j\right] \tag{A64}$$

where all summations refer to $i, j = 1, 2, \ldots, n$, except for restrictions stated. Thus the multiple integral to be evaluated has as the integrand the exponential of a quadratic expression in the u_i which, for sufficiently small θ, is never positive. The integral always exists and is an example of an important standard type, of which (A11–A17) shows the simplest case. The general result can be obtained by an inductive argument from the simple case, but will not be developed here. The result for this special case, in which the coefficient of every u_i^2 is the same and the coefficient of every $u_i u_j (i < j)$ is the same, is that

$$M_{\sum(u_i - \bar{u})^2}(\theta) = D^{-\frac{1}{2}}, \tag{A65}$$

where D is a determinant of n rows and columns such that each diagonal element is the coefficient of u_i^2 and each non-diagonal element is the coefficient of $u_i u_j$. A reader who is not familiar with routine methods for evaluating determinants should consult any standard text. Subtraction of the first row from each other row in turn, followed by addition of all other columns to the first quickly gives the result:

$$D = \begin{vmatrix} 1-2\theta\dfrac{n-1}{n} & \dfrac{2\theta}{n} & \dfrac{2\theta}{n} & \cdots & \dfrac{2\theta}{n} \\[2mm] \dfrac{2\theta}{n} & 1-2\theta\dfrac{n-1}{n} & \dfrac{2\theta}{n} & \cdots & \dfrac{2\theta}{n} \\[2mm] \dfrac{2\theta}{n} & \dfrac{2\theta}{n} & 1-2\theta\dfrac{n-1}{n} & \cdots & \dfrac{2\theta}{n} \\[2mm] \cdot & \cdot & \cdot & & \cdot \\ \cdot & \cdot & \cdot & & \cdot \\ \cdot & \cdot & \cdot & & \cdot \\[2mm] \dfrac{2\theta}{n} & \dfrac{2\theta}{n} & \dfrac{2\theta}{n} & & 1-2\theta\dfrac{n-1}{n} \end{vmatrix}$$

$$= \begin{vmatrix} 1-2\theta\dfrac{n-1}{n} & \dfrac{2\theta}{n} & \dfrac{2\theta}{n} & \cdots & \dfrac{2\theta}{n} \\[2mm] 2\theta-1 & 1-2\theta & 0 & \cdots & 0 \\[1mm] 2\theta-1 & 0 & 1-2\theta & \cdots & 0 \\ \cdot & \cdot & \cdot & & \cdot \\ \cdot & \cdot & \cdot & & \cdot \\ \cdot & \cdot & \cdot & & \cdot \\ 2\theta-1 & 0 & 0 & & 1-2\theta \end{vmatrix}$$

$$= \begin{vmatrix} 1 & \dfrac{2\theta}{n} & \dfrac{2\theta}{n} & \cdots & \dfrac{2\theta}{n} \\[2mm] 0 & 1-2\theta & 0 & \cdots & 0 \\[1mm] 0 & 0 & 1-2\theta & \cdots & 0 \\ \cdot & \cdot & \cdot & & \cdot \\ \cdot & \cdot & \cdot & & \cdot \\ \cdot & \cdot & \cdot & & \cdot \\ 0 & 0 & 0 & & 1-2\theta \end{vmatrix}$$

$$= (1-2\theta)^{n-1}. \tag{A66}$$

Reference to (A58) shows that

$$\sum (x_i - \bar{x})^2 = \sigma^2 \sum (u_i - \bar{u})^2, \tag{A67}$$

and (4.41) leads to

$$M_{\Sigma(x_i-\bar{x})^2}(\theta) = (1-2\sigma^2\theta)^{-(n-1)/2}, \tag{A68}$$

as stated in (9.27). Thus the m.g.f. of $\sum (x_i - \xi)^2$ as stated in (9.22) is the product of those in (A68) and (9.26). The correspondence with the terms on the two sides of equation (9.23) then shows that the two terms on the right-hand side of this equation must be independently distributed; this requires a converse of the theorem represented by equation (5.21) which can be readily proved but is not discussed further here.

※　　　　※　　　　※

A hypersphere of radius r in n dimensions may be defined as the locus of all points X with Cartesian co-ordinates $(x_1, x_2, \ldots, x_n)$ that satisfy

$$x_1^2 + x_2^2 + \ldots + x_n^2 = r^2. \tag{A69}$$

Geometrically, this can be regarded as a figure referred to a set of n rectangular axes such that every point, X, of it is at a 'distance' r from the origin. The geometrical terminology is clearly valid for $n = 2, 3$, and is a convenient aid to imagination and intuition for larger n; anyone who objects to it as unreal can instead adopt a clumsier algebraic language.

The space (area) within a circle of radius r is πr^2, proportional to r^2. The space (volume) within a sphere of radius r is $4\pi r^3/3$, proportional to r^3. These well-known results can be obtained as multiple integrals:

$$\int\!\int dx_1\, dx_2$$

and

$$\int\!\int\!\int dx_1\, dx_2\, dx_3$$

taken over all values of the x_i for which

$$\sum x_i^2 \leqslant r^2 \tag{A70}$$

for $n = 2, 3$ respectively. A similar evaluation of

$$\int\!\int \ldots \int dx_1\, dx_2 \ldots dx_n \tag{A71}$$

for all x_i satisfying (A70) gives the n-dimensional analogue. The transformation

$$x_i = r u_i \tag{A72}$$

shows the result to be

$$r^n \int\!\int \ldots \int du_1\, du_2 \ldots du_n,$$

taken over all u_i satisfying

$$\sum u_i^2 \leqslant 1, \tag{A73}$$

thus establishing the proportionality to r^n. The integration eventually leads to

$$\pi^{n/2} r^n / \Gamma\left(\frac{n+2}{2}\right); \tag{A74}$$

this will not be proved here as the value of the multiplier of r^n is not immediately important. Note that for $n = 1, 2, 3$ the multiplier reduces to $2, \pi, 4\pi/3$, and that the 'volume of a 1-dimensional sphere' is the length of the line between the two solutions of $x_1^2 = r^2$.

※　　　※　　　※

The integration that leads to (9.50) is less difficult than that required for the s^2 distribution, but may still trouble some who are not accustomed to bivariate integrals. The substitution

$$x = st + \xi \tag{A75}$$

(with s^2 retained as the second variate) requires, by the usual Jacobian rule,

$$dx = s\, dt. \tag{A76}$$

Thus the expression (9.49) becomes

$$\text{constant} \times \exp\left[-\frac{t^2 s^2}{2\sigma^2}\right] (s^2)^{\frac{1}{2}f-1} \exp\left[-\frac{fs^2}{2\sigma^2}\right] s\, dt\, d(s^2). \tag{A77}$$

The p.d.f. of t, $f(t)$, is obtainable by averaging this last expression, by integration over the whole range of s^2:

$$f(t) = \text{constant} \times \int_0^\infty (s^2)^{\frac{1}{2}(f-1)} \exp\left[-\frac{s^2}{2\sigma^2}(f+t^2)\right] d(s^2). \tag{A78}$$

The integral to be evaluated is again of the gamma function form, as is discovered by the substitution

$$u = \frac{fs^2}{2\sigma^2}\left(1 + \frac{t^2}{f}\right); \tag{A79}$$

only those parts of the expression involving t or u need be followed exactly, all other factors being absorbed into the constant. Hence

$$f(t) = \text{constant} \times \left(1 + \frac{t^2}{f}\right)^{-\frac{1}{2}(f+1)} \int_0^\infty u^{\frac{1}{2}(k-1)} e^{-u}\, du$$

$$= \text{constant} \times \left(1 + \frac{t^2}{f}\right)^{-\frac{1}{2}(f+1)}. \tag{A80}$$

No attempt has been made here to obtain the constant factor, as stress on this distracts attention from the main steps of the evaluation. Either from

$$\int_{-\infty}^{\infty} f(t)\,dt = 1 \tag{A81}$$

or by keeping track of constant factors throughout, the full result

$$f(t) = (f\pi)^{-\frac{1}{2}}\frac{\Gamma\left(\dfrac{f+1}{2}\right)}{\Gamma\left(\dfrac{f}{2}\right)}\left(1+\frac{t^2}{f}\right)^{-\frac{1}{2}(f+1)} \tag{A82}$$

appears.

✳   ✳   ✳

Consider the last two terms on the right-hand side of (10.10). Expansion and rearrangement give

$$\frac{n_1 n_2}{n_1 + n_2}(\bar{x}_1 - \bar{x}_2)^2 + (n_1 + n_2)(\bar{x} - \xi)^2$$

$$= \frac{n_1 n_2}{n_1 + n_2}(\bar{x}_1^2 - 2\bar{x}_1 \bar{x}_2 + \bar{x}_2^2)$$

$$\quad + (n_1 + n_2)\left[\frac{n_1^2 \bar{x}_1^2 + 2n_1 n_2 \bar{x}_1 \bar{x}_2 + n_2^2 \bar{x}_2^2}{(n_1 + n_2)^2} - \frac{2(n_1 \bar{x}_1 + n_2 \bar{x}_2)}{n_1 + n_2}\xi + \xi^2\right]$$

$$= \bar{x}_1^2\left(\frac{n_1 n_2}{n_1 + n_2} + \frac{n_1^2}{n_1 + n_2}\right) + \bar{x}_2^2\left(\frac{n_1 n_2}{n_1 + n_2} + \frac{n_2^2}{n_1 + n_2}\right)$$

$$\quad - 2(n_1 \bar{x}_1 + n_2 \bar{x}_2)\xi + (n_1 + n_2)\xi^2$$

$$= n_1(\bar{x}_1 - \xi)^2 + n_2(\bar{x}_2 - \xi)^2. \tag{A83}$$

Hence (10.10) follows as a sum of two relations like (9.24).

✳   ✳   ✳

The example in section 11.12 is typical of situations in which Normally distributed observations can be represented by linear models. Write x_{ijk} for the measurement made on the rat in row i, column j of Table 11.2 or Table 11.14, where $i = 1, 2, \ldots, 8$, $j = 1, 2, 3, 4$, and k indicates the treatment (A, B, C, D). Suppose that each x_{ijk} is Normally distributed about its expectation ξ_{ijk} with variance σ^2 independent of all suffixes. That is to say

$$x_{ijk} = \xi_{ijk} + \epsilon_{ijk}, \tag{A84}$$

where ϵ_{ijk} is $N(0, \sigma^2)$. A linear model postulates that ξ_{ijk} is the general mean for the treatment k modified by the addition of components for the particular row and column, these components being independent of one another and of the treatment. This requires definition of τ_k as the treatment mean for treatment k and of ρ_i, γ_j as row and column components for the various i, j. The linear model then means that ξ_{ijk} can be expressed as a sum of appropriate members of these three sets of parameters:

$$\xi_{ijk} = \rho_i + \gamma_j + \tau_k. \tag{A85}$$

Without loss of generality, one may take

$$\left. \begin{array}{l} \displaystyle\sum_{i=1}^{8} \rho_i = 0, \\[2ex] \displaystyle\sum_{j=1}^{4} \gamma_j = 0, \end{array} \right\} \tag{A86}$$

because any alternative can be absorbed into the values of the treatment parameters, τ_k: only differences between the τ_k can be discussed, so that indeterminacy of the separate values to the extent of an additive constant is unimportant.

If the calculations that led to Table 11.16 are repeated in symbols, one can prove that the statistical expectations of the several sums of squares are:

Rows	$7\sigma^2 + 4 \sum \rho_i^2$	(A87)
Columns	$3\sigma^2 + 8 \sum \gamma_j^2$	(A88)
Treatments	$3\sigma^2 + 8 \sum (\tau_k - \bar\tau)^2$	(A89)
Residual	$18\sigma^2$	(A90)

where each summation is over the corresponding suffix and

$$\bar\tau = \sum \tau_k / 4. \tag{A91}$$

The proof involves tedious but straightforward algebra. For example, the total of column 1 (97 in Table 11.15) is in symbols

$$8\gamma_1 + 8\bar\tau + \text{sum of 8 different } \epsilon\text{'s,} \tag{A92}$$

because (A86) and the character of the design cause the ρ components to vanish. The other columns differ in the γ_j and have entirely different ϵ's. The procedure of (11.8) can be followed with these expressions; the expectation is obtained by substituting σ^2 for each ϵ^2 and 0 for each product of two ϵ's (because they are independent). The interested reader should have no difficulty in completing this and the similar steps, but must beware of forgetting the adjustment for the mean!

In each of (A87–A90), the coefficient of σ^2 is the number of degrees of freedom shown in Table 11.16. Hence the expectation of each *mean square* begins with σ^2, and for the first three adds to this a non-negative quadratic function of one of the sets of parameters. From (A89), the expected mean square for treatments is equal to σ^2 if and only if all τ_k are equal and otherwise is greater. The tests of significance used towards the end of section 11.12 then follow. The reader will find it instructive to try to generalise (A84–A92) for a design consisting of two or more Latin squares of arbitrary (but equal) size, to obtain corresponding formulae for Tables 11.1, 11.3, and to see where the same simple argument breaks down for Table 11.8 (as a result of non-orthogonality). If he can do all this without further instruction, he is manifesting great ability in one field of statistics!

※   ※   ※

Suppose that a, b, n are positive integers for which

$$n \leqslant a+b. \tag{A93}$$

The number of ways in which n can be chosen from $(a+b)$ is

$$\binom{a+b}{n}. \tag{A94}$$

For any positive integer x with

$$x \leqslant n$$

the number of ways of choosing x out of a and $(n-x)$ out of b is

$$\binom{a}{x}\binom{b}{n-x}, \tag{A95}$$

where the symbol $\binom{u}{v}$ is defined to be zero if $v > u$. Now choice of n from $(a+b)$ can be achieved only by having x out of a and $(n-x)$ out of b for some x, and therefore the expression (A94) must equal the sum of (A95) over all possible n:

$$\frac{\displaystyle\sum_{x=0}^{n} \binom{a}{x}\binom{b}{n-x}}{\binom{a+b}{n}} = 1. \tag{A96}$$

The expression (A95) is non-negative, and therefore the $(n+1)$ terms on the left of (A96) can be taken as defining a discrete p.d.f. (known as the *hypergeometric distribution*). Now define new parameters θ_1, θ_2 by

$$\left.\begin{array}{l} a = -\theta_1/\theta_2 \\ b = -(1-\theta_1)/\theta_2 \end{array}\right\}. \tag{A97}$$

The typical term is:

$$\Pr(x) = \frac{a!}{x!(a-x)!}\frac{b!}{(n-x)!(b-n+x)!}\frac{n!(a+b-n)!}{(a+b)!}$$

$$= \binom{n}{x}\frac{a(a-1)(a-2)\ldots(a-x+1)\,b(b-1)(b-2)\ldots(b-n+x+1)}{(a+b)(a+b-1)\ldots(a+b-n+1)}, \tag{A98}$$

and substitution from (A97) gives (12.7). A more general proof can be given to cover the case of a, b non-integral, but is not presented here.

❊   ❊   ❊

That (12.15), (12.16) are sufficient to secure consistency of t is readily proved. By (6.45), whatever the distribution of t, for an arbitrary positive quantity a

$$\Pr[|t-\mu_1(t)| < a] > 1-\frac{\mu_2(t)}{a^2}. \tag{A99}$$

But

$$|t-\mu_1(t)| < a \tag{A100}$$

implies

$$|t-\theta| < a+|\mu_1(t)-\theta| \tag{A101}$$

for any θ. Therefore

$$\Pr[|t-\theta| < a+|\mu_1(t)-\theta|] > 1-\frac{\mu_2(t)}{a^2}. \tag{A102}$$

Now (12.15), (12.16) ensure that $|\mu_1(t)-\theta|$ and $\mu_2(t)$ can be made arbitrarily small by the condition $n>n^*$ for some suitable n^*. Hence a, n^* can always be determined so as to make (A102) equivalent to (12.12). The argument can easily be written *in extenso* in the formal language of limits. An analogous proof shows that (12.15), (12.16) are necessary conditions.

❊   ❊   ❊

With s^2 as defined in (9.9),

$$E(s^2) = \sigma^2 \equiv \mu_2(x) \tag{A103}$$

whatever the distribution. There is no general result for $E(s)$. If the distribution of the x_i is Normal, integration over the p.d.f. represented by the first factor in (9.40) gives

$$E(s) = \left(\frac{2}{n-1}\right)^{\frac{1}{2}} \frac{\Gamma\left(\frac{n}{2}\right)}{\Gamma\left(\frac{n-1}{2}\right)} \sigma; \tag{A104}$$

the two integrals needed both become essentially gamma functions after substituting $s^2 = u$. Therefore

$$t = \left(\frac{n-1}{2}\right)^{\frac{1}{2}} \frac{\Gamma\left(\frac{n-1}{2}\right)}{\Gamma\left(\frac{n}{2}\right)} s \tag{A105}$$

is an unbiased estimator of σ.

※ ※ ※

Evidently

$$E(x) = \int_0^\infty \frac{x}{\theta} e^{-x/\theta} \, dx$$

$$= \theta \tag{A106}$$

after integration by parts. Similarly

$$E(x^2) = \int_0^\infty \frac{x^2}{\theta} e^{x/\theta} \, dx$$

$$= 2\theta^2 \tag{A107}$$

and therefore

$$Var(x) = 2\theta^2 - \theta^2 = \theta^2. \tag{A108}$$

For a sample of n independent values x_i,

$$E(\Sigma x) = nE(x) \tag{A109}$$

$$Var(\Sigma x) = n \, Var(x) \tag{A110}$$

and (12.22), (12.23) follow.

※ ※ ※

The integration required is somewhat beyond the level of this text, but will be outlined here. The probability that a single observation is less than or equal to X is

$$\int_0^X f(x|\theta)\,dx = e^{-X/\theta}. \tag{A111}$$

Now for t to be the median of a sample of $(2m+1)$ observations, m observations must be less than or equal to t, 1 must lie in $(t, t+dt)$, and m must be greater than or equal to $(t+dt)$. The probability of this can be written down by an obvious extension of the binomial probability (4.10) to the *trinomial*

$$\frac{(2m+1)!}{m!\,1!\,m!}\,(e^{-t/\theta})^m \left(\frac{1}{\theta}e^{-t/\theta}\,dt\right)[1-e^{-(t+dt)/\theta}]^m. \tag{A112}$$

The p.d.f. of t, $g(t|\theta)$, is obtained by expressing this to the first order in dt, and is

$$g(t) = \frac{(2m+1)!}{(m!)^2}\,\theta^{-1}e^{-(m+1)t/\theta}(1-e^{-t/\theta})^m. \tag{A113}$$

The next step is to find the m.g.f. of t. Since θ is in use as a parameter, α will here be used as the 'dummy' required in the m.g.f. Then

$$M_t(\alpha) = \int_0^\infty e^{\alpha t} g(t)\,dt. \tag{A114}$$

After the substitution

$$y = e^{-t/\theta}, \tag{A115}$$

this becomes

$$M_t(\alpha) = \frac{(2m+1)!}{(m!)^2}\int_0^1 y^{m-\alpha\theta}(1-y)^m\,dy. \tag{A116}$$

This integral is of a standard form allied to the gamma function (section 9.4), and its evaluation is discussed in standard texts on mathematical analysis. The result is

$$M_t(\alpha) = \frac{(2m+1)!}{(m!)^2}\frac{\Gamma(m+1)\,\Gamma(m+1-\alpha\theta)}{\Gamma(2m+2-\alpha\theta)}$$

$$= \left[\left(1-\frac{\alpha\theta}{m+1}\right)\left(1-\frac{\alpha\theta}{m+2}\right)\left(1-\frac{\alpha\theta}{m+3}\right)\cdots\left(1-\frac{\alpha\theta}{2m+1}\right)\right]^{-1}, \tag{A117}$$

the simplification following by use of (9.18) and cancellation of factors in numerator and denominator. Expansion of (A117) as a power series in α as far as the terms in α, α^2 then leads to μ_1', μ_2' for the distribution of t; (12.24) and (12.26) readily follow.

※　　　　　※　　　　　※

A well-known theorem on infinite series states that

$$\sum_{j=1}^{J} \frac{1}{j} - \log_e J \to \gamma \quad \text{as } J \to \infty, \tag{A118}$$

where γ is a quantity known as *Euler's constant*. Hence

$$\sum_{m+1}^{2m+1} \frac{1}{j} - \log_e \left(\frac{2m+1}{m+1} \right) \to 0 \quad \text{as } m \to \infty, \tag{A119}$$

and (12.25) follows.

※　　　　　※　　　　　※

For the example in section 11.12, the method of least squares involves writing (12.47) as

$$S = \sum (x_{ijk} - \rho_i - \gamma_j - \tau_k)^2 \tag{A120}$$

where $\sum$ denotes summation over all the 32 combinations of i, j, k that occur. The constraints (A86) must be remembered; they can be used to eliminate ρ_8, γ_4 or, more symmetrically, Lagrange multipliers can be employed. Estimation of the treatment parameters leads to minimisation conditions of the form

$$\frac{\partial S}{\partial \tau_A} = -2 \sum_A (x_{ijA} - \rho_i - \gamma_j - \tau_A) = 0, \tag{A121}$$

where $\sum_A$ denotes summation over the eight combinations of i, j, k that relate to rats on treatment A. In the summation, each ρ_i occurs once and each γ_j occurs twice, so that the totals of these terms is zero. Hence t_A, the least squares estimator of τ_A, satisfies

$$\sum_A x_{ijA} - 8 t_A = 0. \tag{A122}$$

This equation does not involve any unknown except t_A, and clearly

$$t_A = \sum_A x_{ijA}/8. \tag{A123}$$

Thus each treatment parameter is estimated by the simple mean for the eight rats on the treatment. Analogous results are obtainable for the other parameters.

If the experiment had been less symmetrical, or if mishaps cause results for three of the 32 rats to be unavailable, the method still applies but (A122) becomes more complicated. Indeed (A122) might then involve all the t_k as well as the r_i and g_j, the estimators of the other parameters, and the final step would be solution of a set of linear equations (in 14 variables).

❋   ❋   ❋

As a simpler illustration, consider the situation in which a population of circles is to be considered (to a reasonable approximation, cross-sections of pieces of wire, cross-sections of pine trees, or zones in which bacterial growth is inhibited when a drop of penicillin is placed upon a culture plate inoculated with bacteria). One technique might measure the diameters of n circles (x_i), a second might measure areas (y_i), and

$$y_i = \pi x_i^2/4. \tag{A124}$$

If the population mean and variance for the diameters are θ, σ^2 respectively (with no limitation to Normality),

$$E(x_i) = \theta, \tag{A125}$$

$$E(y_i) = \pi(\theta^2 + \sigma^2)/4. \tag{A126}$$

The method of least squares applied to diameters leads to the estimator t_1 of θ, where

$$t_1 = \sum x_i/n. \tag{A127}$$

Applied to areas, however, it gives the estimator t_2 (assuming σ^2 to be known), where

$$t_2 = \left(\frac{4 \sum y_i}{n\pi} - \sigma^2\right)^{\frac{1}{2}}. \tag{A128}$$

This is equivalent to

$$t_2 = \left(\frac{\sum x_i^2}{n} - \sigma^2\right)^{\frac{1}{2}}. \tag{A129}$$

Evidently t_1 and t_2 are not identical. (If the parameter σ^2 is also unknown, further complications enter.)

❋   ❋   ❋

The reader who is worried by the arbitrariness of C may like to note that the accepted definition is

$$C = 1/L(t_L), \tag{A130}$$

where t_L is as defined in section 12.12.

* * *

By differentiation of (12.59),

$$\frac{\partial}{\partial\theta_1}\log L = \Sigma\,(x-\theta_1)/\theta_2 = 0, \tag{A131}$$

$$\frac{\partial}{\partial\theta_2}\log L = -\frac{n}{2\theta_2}+\frac{\Sigma\,(x-\theta_1)^2}{2\theta_2^2} = 0, \tag{A132}$$

and the solutions (12.60), (12.61) are obvious.

* * *

Proof of the Cramér–Rao inequality is necessarily somewhat lengthy. It uses an important lemma commonly known as *Schwarz's inequality*, which has both a discrete and a continuous form. Suppose that g_j, h_j, for $j=1, 2, \ldots, p$, are any real quantities. Let a be an arbitrary real number. Evidently

$$\sum_j (ag_j+h_j)^2 \geqslant 0 \tag{A133}$$

for all a. This inequality may be expanded as

$$a^2\sum_j g_j^2+2a\sum_j g_j h_j+\Sigma\, h_j^2 \geqslant 0. \tag{A134}$$

As is well known, necessary and sufficient conditions for truth of the inequality

$$Aa^2+2Ba+C \geqslant 0 \tag{A135}$$

for all real a are

$$A \geqslant 0, \tag{A136}$$

$$AC \geqslant B^2. \tag{A137}$$

In (A134), the truth of (A136) is obvious; (A137) gives

$$\left(\sum_j g_j^2\right)\left(\sum_j h_j^2\right) \geqslant (\Sigma\, g_j h_j^2)^2 \tag{A138}$$

with equality holding only if g_j/h_j is constant for all j. This is the discrete form of Schwarz's inequality. The continuous form relates to functions

$g(u)$, $h(u)$ whose squares and product are integrable over a finite or infinite range. An exactly parallel argument proves that, for integration over this range,

$$\int [g(u)]^2 \, du \int [h(u)]^2 \, du \geqslant \left[\int g(u) \, h(u) \, du \right]^2. \qquad \text{(A139)}$$

Turn now to the theorem. The probability element associated with a particular sample, that is to say the joint probability of an observation in the interval $(x_i, x_i + dx_i)$ for all i, is

$$f(x_1|\theta)f(x_2|\theta)\ldots f(x_n|\theta) \, dx_1 \, dx_2 \ldots dx_n. \qquad \text{(A140)}$$

As an abbreviation of notation, represent the sample of n values of x_i as X, and write (A140) as

$$\phi(X|\theta) \, dX \qquad \text{(A141)}$$

or where there is no fear of misunderstanding simply as

$$\phi \, dX. \qquad \text{(A142)}$$

Also, from here to (A154) use the notation $\int \ldots dX$ to represent a multiple integral with respect to all of the x_i over the full range of values permitted to the variate x. Nothing more than convenience of notation is implied here, and anyone confused by expressions such as (A142) or integrals taken with respect to X can immediately rewrite them in full in the form corresponding to (A140). Evidently ϕ, the product of n particular values of the original p.d.f., can be regarded as a function of θ; write

$$\phi' = \frac{d\phi}{d\theta}, \qquad \text{(A143)}$$

$$\phi'' = \frac{d^2\phi}{d\theta^2}. \qquad \text{(A144)}$$

A generalisation of (4.26) shows that

$$\int \phi \, dX = 1, \qquad \text{(A145)}$$

whence, by differentiation, for all θ

$$\int \phi' \, dX = 0, \qquad \text{(A146)}$$

$$\int \phi'' \, dX = 0. \qquad \text{(A147)}$$

Now suppose that t is any statistic (that is to say a function of the x_i) which is an unbiased estimator of θ. The equation (12.71) means

$$\int t\phi \, dX = \theta. \qquad \text{(A148)}$$

Since t is *not* a function of θ, differentiation gives

$$\int t\phi' \, dX = 1. \tag{A149}$$

Multiplication of (A146) by θ and subtraction from (A149) gives

$$1 = \int (t-\theta)\phi' \, dX \tag{A150}$$

$$= \int (t-\theta)\frac{d}{d\theta}(\log \phi)\phi \, dX \quad \text{as is easily verified}$$

$$= \int [(t-\theta)\phi^{\frac{1}{2}}]\left[\frac{d}{d\theta}(\log \phi)\phi^{\frac{1}{2}}\right] dX. \tag{A151}$$

Application of (A139) then gives

$$\int (t-\theta)^2 \phi \, dX \int \left[\frac{d}{d\theta}(\log \phi)\right]^2 \phi \, dX \geqslant 1, \tag{A152}$$

the first factor on the left being by definition $Var(t)$. As may be verified by performing the differentiations,

$$\left[\frac{d}{d\theta}(\log \phi)\right]^2 = \frac{\phi''}{\phi} - \frac{d^2}{d\theta^2}(\log \phi)$$

$$= \frac{\phi''}{\phi} - \sum_i \frac{d^2}{d\theta^2}[\log f(x_i|\theta)], \tag{A153}$$

because of the definition of ϕ. Multiplication by ϕ and integration gives, using (A147),

$$\int \left[\frac{d}{d\theta}(\log \phi)\right]^2 \phi \, dX = -\int \sum_i \frac{d^2}{d\theta^2}[\log f(x_i|\theta)]\phi \, dX. \tag{A154}$$

The right-hand side of (A154) involves the sum of n terms, of which a typical one (the second) may be written more fully as

$$\int \frac{d^2}{d\theta^2}[\log f(x_2|\theta)]f(x_1|\theta)f(x_2|\theta)\ldots f(x_n|\theta) \, dx_1 \, dx_2 \ldots dx_n. \tag{A155}$$

Integration of this over $x_1, x_3, \ldots, x_n$ simply gives a factor unity each time, by virtue of (4.26), and therefore (A155) becomes the simple integral

$$\int \frac{d^2}{d\theta^2}[\log f(x_2|\theta)]f(x_2|\theta) \, dx_2. \tag{A156}$$

But (A156) is independent of the suffix, and the n terms in the summation are all equal to

$$\int \frac{d^2}{d\theta^2}[\log f(x|\theta)]f(x|\theta) \, dx. \tag{A157}$$

Combination of (A152), (A154), and (A157) then immediately gives (12.72).

※   ※   ※

For the Cauchy distribution, from (12.69),

$$\log f = -\log \pi - \log [1+(x-\theta)^2] \tag{A158}$$

and

$$\frac{d}{d\theta}(\log f) = \frac{2(x-\theta)}{1+(x-\theta)^2}, \tag{A159}$$

so that

$$\frac{d^2}{d\theta^2}(\log f) = \frac{-2}{1+(x-\theta)^2} + \frac{4(x-\theta)^2}{[1+(x-\theta)^2]^2}, \tag{A160}$$

which can be arranged as (12.77).

The substitution

$$x-\theta = \tan u \tag{A161}$$

gives

$$\pi \int_{-\infty}^{\infty} f \frac{d^2}{d\theta^2}(\log f)\, dx = 2 \int_{-\infty}^{\infty} \frac{dx}{[1+(x-\theta)^2]^2} - 4 \int_{-\infty}^{\infty} \frac{dx}{[1+(x-\theta)^2]^3}$$

$$= 2 \int_{-\pi/2}^{\pi/2} \cos^2 u\, du - 4 \int_{-\pi/2}^{\pi/2} \cos^4 u\, du$$

$$= \pi - \frac{3\pi}{2}$$

$$= -\pi/2. \tag{A162}$$

※   ※   ※

Differentiation of $S(\alpha, \beta)$ in (12.82) gives

$$\frac{\partial S}{\partial \alpha} = -2 \sum (x-\alpha-\beta u), \tag{A163}$$

$$\frac{\partial S}{\partial \beta} = -2 \sum u(x-\alpha-\beta u), \tag{A164}$$

where the suffixes on x, u are omitted for simplicity and $\sum$ always denotes summation over the n observations. The maximum likelihood estimators a, b are obtained as the values of α, β that make these differential coefficients zero. Hence (remember that $\Sigma a = na$),

$$na + b \Sigma u = \Sigma x, \tag{A165}$$

$$a \Sigma u + b \Sigma u^2 = \Sigma ux. \tag{A166}$$

Multiplication of (A165) by $\Sigma u/n$ and subtraction from (A166) gives

$$b \left[\Sigma u^2 - \frac{(\Sigma u)^2}{n} \right] = \Sigma ux - \frac{\Sigma u \Sigma x}{n}, \tag{A167}$$

whence (12.85) follows. Division of (A165) by n shows that, when b has been determined, a can be found from (12.84).

✳   ✳   ✳

FURTHER READING

The student wishing to read further for himself will find many books available at a mathematical standard slightly higher than that required here. Among the better ones are:

BIRNBAUM, Z. W. 1962. *Introduction to Probability and Mathematical Statistics.* New York: Harper.

FRASER, D. A. S. 1959. *Statistics, An Introduction.* New York: Wiley.

FREEMAN, H. 1963. *Introduction to Statistical Inference.* Reading, Massachusetts: Addison-Wesley.

HOEL, P. G. 1962. *Introduction to Mathematical Statistics* (3rd edition). New York: Wiley.

For more general reading, requiring little mathematics but educating the reader in the uses of statistics, and helping the student to decide whether the statistical profession has any attraction for him, the following are strongly recommended:

BROOKES, B. C., and DICK, W. F. L., 1951. *Introduction to Statistical Method.* London: Heinemann.

HUFF, D. 1954. *How to Lie with Statistics.* London: Gollancz.

MENDENHALL, W. 1964. *Introduction to Statistics.* Belmont, California: Wadsworth.

MORONEY, M. J. 1956. *Facts from Figures* (3rd edition). London: Penguin Books.

There also exist many books on methods of statistical analysis and their applications in particular sciences, in industry and commerce, and so on. These may seem at first rather dull to the mathematician who lacks knowledge of the fields of application; appropriate ones of course need to be studied at a later stage by a student intending to work in such a field, by which time he should find his interest reinforced by increasing understanding of the practical aims.

INDEX